INTRODUCTION TO STATISTICS

WITH THE WOLFRAM LANGUAGE

INTRODUCTION TO STATISTICS

WITH THE WOLFRAM LANGUAGE

JUAN H. KLOPPER

WolframMedia

Introduction to Statistics with the Wolfram Language
by Juan H. Klopper

Copyright © 2020 by Wolfram Media, Inc.

Wolfram Media, Inc.
wolfram-media.com
ISBN 978-1-57955-033-2 (paperback)
ISBN 978-1-57955-034-9 (ebook)

For information about permission to reproduce selections from this book, write to permissions@wolfram.com.

Library of Congress Cataloging-in-Publication Data

Names: Klopper, Juan H., 1969- author.
Title: Introduction to statistics with the Wolfram language / Juan H. Klopper.
Description: Champaign : Wolfram Media, Inc., [2020] | Includes index.
Identifiers: LCCN 2020034690 (print) | LCCN 2020034691 (ebook) |
ISBN 9781579550332 (paperback) | ISBN 9781579550349 (epub)
Subjects: LCSH: Mathematical statistics—Data processing. |
Wolfram language (Computer program language)
Classification: LCC QA276.4 .K59 2020 (print) | LCC QA276.4 (ebook) |
DDC 519.50285/5133—dc23
LC record available at https://lccn.loc.gov/2020034690
LC ebook record available at https://lccn.loc.gov/2020034691

Typesetting and page production were completed using Wolfram Notebooks.

Table of Contents

1 | An Introduction to Data Analysis Using the Wolfram Language

Introduction to This Text

This text will teach you a practical, useful, and modern approach to analysing data. In this first chapter, I will aim to give a quick and useful overview of doing data analysis using the Wolfram Language. With today's modern computational tools, statistics and data analysis can be easy to use and very exciting to learn.

The Wolfram Language is a powerful and modern computer language, and Chapters 2–4 will get you up and running with the language. Let me use this introduction to allay your fears about computer languages. Though it is not necessary to learn a computer language to learn statistics, learning this computer language will help you learn statistics faster. It will even provide you with the power to start using statistics immediately in your own life.

Once you become familiar with speaking your new language, we will use it throughout the rest of the text to explain statistical concepts in a way that is much easier than trying to understand esoteric equations. Together we will learn what the equations mean and how simple it is to do the calculations.

> To read the Wolfram Notebook version of this book and perform the exercises, you will need Mathematica (wolfram.com/mathematica/trial) or the free Wolfram Player. Several exercises and graphics use data I have provided in the form of sample .csv files. You will not need to open or alter the .csv files; just evaluate the notebook version of each chapter and it will load the appropriate file. Go to wolfr.am/klopper and click "Download Notebooks" to download the files for free.

Motivation

Knowledge of statistics is the ability to understand the story that data tries to tell. As with all storytelling, it is most important to know the language. The most beautiful poems, your favourite song lyrics, and award-winning novels mean nothing without understanding the language in which they are written. The stories hidden in rows and columns of data can be just as captivating and arguably more important than all the prose in the the world. The ability to work with data through the language of statistics and data analysis is key to your success in many modern-day careers.

It has never been simpler to learn the language of data. The number of software tools available today, of which the Wolfram Language is an excellent example, is indeed an embarrassment of riches. If you have never learned a computing language before, the Wolfram Language is "natural language" based, providing access to social science researchers who may find coding in more complicated languages to be too intimidating. Moreover, as the Wolfram Language is not primarily statistics software, with it you'll be able to do far more complex analysis, visualizations of data, and even app programming for web deployment.

This text does not contain the traditional approach to teaching statistics (an approach that has alienated so many from this subject). Just as computer keyboards and cell-phone screens have replaced pencil and paper by way of their ubiquity, simplicity, and ease of use, these languages have replaced the old-fashioned way of introducing the exciting world of statistics and data analysis.

For a more complete overview of the Wolfram Language, I recommend Stephen Wolfram's book *An Elementary Introduction to the Wolfram Language* (2017), available online at no cost here: wolfr.am/eiwl.

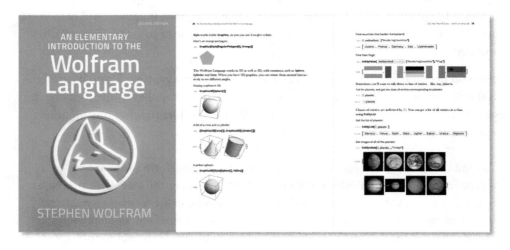

Who Is This Book For?

Everyone. The ability to do data analysis is no longer just for university researchers and business analysts. Our modern world is made up of data. From being locked away behind academic walls, libraries, and expensive encyclopedias to reaching us through the trickle feed of newspapers, magazines, radio, and broadcast television, it now lives in our pockets and at our fingertips. Our ability to generate, capture, and store data has exploded. There is currently nothing that is as empowering as the ability to analyse and understand data, so, simply put, this book is for *you*.

A Brief Look at Statistical Data Analysis

You will see in Chapter 6 why humans are bad at making sense of reams of data. If you have ever gazed upon a spreadsheet filled with numbers, you will know what I am talking about. As it turns out, we need to summarize data in order to get to grips with it.

Here we see two long lists of the monetary value of sales made by two salespeople over the course of a year. Imagine that the salespeople are named Sue and Simon.

We begin by entering the data:

In[1]:= **Sue = {**6819, 1328, 2277, 2730, 3313, 2061, 4311, 2110, 4550, 6396, 4587, 2782, 4130, 1517, 2830, 4517, 2580, 1833, 3936, 1855, 1501, 6927, 6072, 1379, 7218, 6569, 1927, 4712, 6918, 3911, 2050, 4278, 1908, 5392, 6962, 1490, 7204, 4992, 6444, 5694, 2127, 4824, 3158, 5706, 5695, 5926, 1734, 6019, 1407, 3453, 6603, 1948, 3695, 2164, 4836, 2130, 4790, 5254, 7030, 6948, 3596, 1952, 4298, 6993, 4979, 2418, 5539, 2514, 1868, 6839, 5469, 2761, 3440, 2445, 5103, 5942, 6361, 1556, 6869, 6278, 4583, 6127, 4848, 5620, 3873, 4081, 5048, 5846, 6964, 4040, 5505, 1659, 3291, 6624, 5580, 6823, 3172, 6629, 6738, 4463, 3126, 5848, 5727, 3032, 4358, 6978, 4772, 5676, 5066, 5372, 7128, 6750, 1379, 3237, 7019, 2690, 1991, 3009, 4487, 1384, 1799, 2782, 3148, 2001, 4192, 3636, 2854, 3255, 1709, 2733, 6289, 7002, 4413, 5775, 3448, 4424, 5554, 3320, 4211, 4487, 6585, 3555, 2576, 4965, 2841, 6653, 2935, 4451, 2712, 3096, 6141, 5198, 4737, 6796, 2112, 1224, 2762, 6553, 4783, 6589, 3912, 2714, 1873, 3967, 2438, 2580, 4389, 2312, 2033, 6240, 2504, 3959, 2359, 2378, 1834, 4733, 1319, 4955, 6327, 4629, 6092, 6280, 4313, 2034, 2190, 2846, 2793, 2889, 1958, 5016, 5667, 3590, 5720, 6617, 4201, 2710, 6981, 3107, 3887, 2733, 3362, 3598, 4491, 5204, 3835, 1371, 6358, 4883, 4879, 3988, 5472, 4567, 4487, 5532, 4026, 5839, 2369, 3411, 4898, 1641, 6069, 1567**};**

In[2]:= **Simon = {**3176, 6952, 2206, 1723, 5802, 1187, 6228, 3988, 6565, 2490, 7031, 5734, 3482, 2010, 6226, 5764, 4466, 5951, 2668, 3558, 2153, 3875, 4712, 4402, 4400, 7043, 3071, 4188, 6378, 3411, 3661, 1957, 1896, 5056, 1204, 3555, 4230, 4112, 5136, 7039, 2063, 2746, 6692, 2903, 4681, 2486, 4876, 5767, 6798, 3368, 4619, 6665, 3296, 4894, 1400, 4101, 4159, 6578, 3063, 3290, 5003, 4507, 6637, 2460, 5596, 4905, 2203, 3556, 5743, 3658, 6294, 5857, 5223, 4511, 6669, 4710, 5165, 3148, 4793, 5384, 1674, 3444, 1843, 7041, 6816, 4102, 4106, 4950, 4832, 2566, 6563, 5783, 1951, 5467, 4521, 5863, 4062, 3120, 1554, 1941, 4794, 5462, 5729, 2272, 1673, 3578, 6661, 2075, 7072, 1342, 5954, 5223, 3414, 5853, 4878, 5864, 2461, 7059, 6861, 4609, 3881, 6324, 1933, 6483, 4031, 1633, 1678, 2584, 1586, 3380, 5880, 2959, 3523, 1682, 6336, 5892, 6729, 1918, 3775, 5815, 2736, 6679, 4301, 3503, 2965, 3235, 1627, 5111, 5898, 5497, 3819, 3818, 1241, 4241, 5907, 4054, 3067, 6205, 2050, 3031, 5581, 2115, 1185, 3145, 5063, 2615, 1245, 5199, 4905, 4289, 3417, 3662, 6444, 3682, 4514, 2164, 2271, 2642, 7001, 6252, 6026, 5215, 3563, 1794, 5182, 2750, 3220, 3157, 2287, 7038, 3790, 3860, 1663, 3552, 1848, 3217, 6947, 1124, 2791, 2424**};**

Be honest. Can you figure out who had the most sales or who had the highest average sales? What was the smallest sale value or the highest? I can't!

The Wolfram Language to the rescue.

Let's have a look at the number of sales made by Sue and Simon:

In[3]:= **Length[Sue]**

Out[3]= 222

In[4]:= **Length[Simon]**

Out[4]= 200

With two simple lines of code, we note that Sue made 222 sales and Simon lagged behind with 200.

Let's see what the average sale values were:

In[5]:= **N[Mean[Sue]]**

Out[5]= 4182.17

In[6]:= **N[Mean[Simon]]**

Out[6]= 4150.16

That was a close call, with Sue just beating Simon. We can also look at the spread of data. One common way of doing this is by looking at the range. This is simply the maximum minus the minimum value.

Here are some data points we can get with Min and Max:

In[7]:= **Min[Sue]**

Out[7]= 1224

In[8]:= **Max[Sue]**

Out[8]= 7218

In[9]:= **Max[Sue] – Min[Sue]**

Out[9]= 5994

In[10]:= **Min[Simon]**

Out[10]= 1124

In[11]:= **Max[Simon]**

Out[11]= 7072

In[12]:= **Max[Simon] – Min[Simon]**

Out[12]= 5948

A proper statistical way of looking at the spread of sale values is the standard deviation. This is the average difference between each value and the mean.

It only takes a single line of code for each person:

In[13]:= **N[StandardDeviation[Sue]]**

Out[13]= **1743.58**

In[14]:= **N[StandardDeviation[Simon]]**

Out[14]= **1708.55**

Another easy way to understand data is to visualize it. The Wolfram Language has one of the richest sets of visualization tools available in modern machine languages. One plot that you might have come across before is the box-and-whisker plot. Plotting is covered in Chapter 7, where you will learn both how to interpret plots and how to create them.

Let's have a look at a box-and-whisker plot showing the sales made by Sue and Simon:

In[15]:= **BoxWhiskerChart[{Sue, Simon}, "Outliers", ChartLabels → {"Sue", "Simon"},**
    PlotLabel → "Sales for the year", ChartStyle → 24]

Yet another way to visualize the sales of our intrepid pair of salespeople is a distribution plot.

Use the Wolfram Language's SmoothHistogram function to achieve this:

In[16]:= **SmoothHistogram[{Sue, Simon}, Filling → Axis,**
    PlotLabel → "Sales for the year", PlotLegends → {"Sue", "Simon"}]

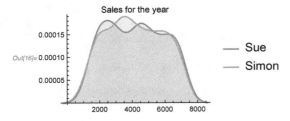

A more statistical way to look at our data is to compare the sale values by Sue and Simon. Although Sue had more sales, a common question might be if this difference was indeed statistically significant. Here we use a nonparametric test called the Mann–Whitney U-test to answer this question. We tell the Wolfram Language to use a significance value of 0.05 (5%).

Use the Wolfram Language to calculate a *p*-value:

In[17]:= **MannWhitneyTest[{Sue, Simon}, SignificanceLevel → 0.05]**

Out[17]= 0.897284

We note a very nonsignificant difference between the two sets of sale values by virtue of the large *p*-value.

We can even use the Wolfram Language to print this statement for us:

In[18]:= **MannWhitneyTest[{Sue, Simon}, 0, "TestConclusion"]**

Out[18]= The null hypothesis that the median difference is 0
    is not rejected at the 5 percent level based on the Mann-Whitney test.

In Chapter 9, we will learn all about hypothesis testing, which forms the bedrock of inferential statistics.

Imagine we have data on how many hours Sue spent on the road each month and what the total sale value was for that month. In the next example, we see the data for the last 36 months. Because I firmly believe in the axiom "practice makes perfect," the values used are simulated data (which is very easy to create using the Wolfram Language). Once you know how to, I urge you to create your own datasets for practice.

Make 36 sale values for Sue, taken at random from the integers in the range from $12123 to $20371 using RandomInteger:

In[19]:= **SueMonthlySales = RandomInteger[{12 123, 20 371}, 36]**

Out[19]= {14 157, 19 387, 20 339, 12 750, 16 737, 20 097, 12 305, 16 098, 13 257, 19 710, 16 235, 19 465,
    13 993, 15 344, 18 112, 12 395, 15 200, 13 257, 18 877, 15 912, 19 490, 19 171, 17 181, 12 382,
    16 922, 17 350, 16 038, 12 915, 20 097, 15 287, 15 344, 16 564, 16 688, 20 339, 15 493, 17 168}

Let's do the same for hours traveled, from the range 14 hours to 45 hours:

In[20]:= **SueHours = RandomInteger[{14, 45}, 36]**

Out[20]= {14, 31, 26, 34, 39, 45, 21, 17, 19, 17, 15, 34, 40, 25, 35, 33, 36,
    41, 32, 24, 35, 24, 16, 17, 38, 32, 26, 41, 19, 33, 40, 14, 32, 33, 25, 36}

Let's see if there is a correlation between hours spent and sales made.

We'll create a list plot that plots pairs of values, in this case hours versus sales:

In[21]:= **ListPlot[Table[{SueHours[[n]], SueMonthlySales[[n]]}, {n, 1, Length[SueHours]}]]**

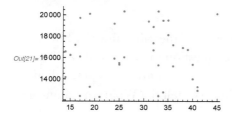

There seems to be little correlation between hours spent and sales made.

It is easy to check on this using a correlation test:

In[22]:= **N[Correlation[SueHours, SueMonthlySales]]**

Out[22]= 0.041366

As you can see, it is almost trivial to do these statistical tests while simultaneously creating beautiful, informative plots.

In the Next Chapter

The examples in this chapter are just a glimpse of what is to come. In the chapters ahead, you will learn about both statistics and how to harness the power of the Wolfram Language to do you calculations.

More to Explore

Wolfram's book is also available as a interactive course on Wolfram U (wolfr.am/t78S9MhK)

Another great resource for Mathematica is C. Hastings, K. Mischo, and M. Morrison's book *Hands-on Start to Wolfram Mathematica* (wolfr.am/t78Zkyf5)

There is also a great Hands-on Start to Mathematica video series (wolfr.am/t793XPz3)

2 | Evaluating Basic Math

Before we learn the language of statistics and data analysis, we will learn a modern computer language called the Wolfram Language. At its core, it is a very powerful calculator with phenomenal number-crunching capabilities. The speed at which it can do this is only limited by your computer architecture. We use a program called Mathematica to write code in the Wolfram Language.

Sometimes, we do simple arithmetic on a handheld calculator. These days, we're all familiar with using a calculator app on a smartphone for the same purpose.

Such simple calculator arithmetic gives us a natural means of introducing the Wolfram Language, which was specifically designed to be easily grasped once you get the hang of the basics. That is to say, the Wolfram Language is consistent and almost everything follows the same pattern. After some use, it becomes easy to guess what a piece of code might have to look like, even though you have not learned explicitly how to write it.

We'll start off this first section with some simple arithmetic.

Addition and Subtraction

Adding the numbers 2 and 2 gives us 4. Just as with the use of a calculator, we simply type the number 2 on the keyboard followed by the plus (+) sign and another 2. To get the solution, simply hold down the shift key while hitting the enter key on a PC or the return key on a Mac.

Use + to add numbers:

```
In[1]:= 2 + 2
```

```
Out[1]= 4
```

The use of the plus (+) sign is simply a convenient syntax for us mere mortals. The Wolfram Language is a functional language built around keywords, termed *functions*. These are built into the language for easy reuse. They are easily identified because they all start with an uppercase letter. Values, termed *arguments*, are passed to the functions, and they all go inside of square brackets ([ ]). Arguments give data or information to the function so as to produce a result.

Addition is accomplished with the Plus function. When you type $2 + 2$, Mathematica actually sees Plus[2, 2]. The two values of 2 are arguments. Note how they are separated by a comma, as all arguments are in general. In the code below, it is easy to see that we want the two arguments to be added, which is what the Plus function does.

You can use Plus to add:

In[2]:= **Plus[2, 2]**

Out[2]= 4

We are not restricted to just adding two numbers. We can add any number of values. In the code below, we use both the Plus function and the convenience syntax.

You can add almost unlimited numbers in this fashion:

In[3]:= **Plus[5, 2, 4, 4]**

Out[3]= 15

In[4]:= **5+2+4+4**

Out[4]= 15

You can also add a string of numbers by using curly braces and Total:

In[5]:= **Total[{5,2,4,4}]**

Out[5]= 15

Here are a few ways to subtract numbers:

In[6]:= **Plus[5, −2]**

Out[6]= 3

In[7]:= **Subtract[5, 2]**

Out[7]= 3

In[8]:= **5−2**

Out[8]= 3

Multiplication and Division

There are many ways to multiply. Probably the most esoteric is the combination of keys necessary to type the multiplication sign (×), which can be created by hitting the esc key (this will create three short, stacked lines on the screen), then the asterisk (∗) symbol, and then the esc key again.

Here are five ways to use the Times function:

In[9]:= **3∗4**

Out[9]= 12

In[10]:= **3 × 4**

Out[10]= 12

In[11]:= **3 × 4**

Out[11]= 12

In[12]:= **Times[3, 4]**

Out[12]= 12

In[13]:= **3 × 4**

Out[13]= 12

Division is accomplished by using the forward slash (/) or the Divide function:

In[14]:= **12/3**

Out[14]= 4

In[15]:= **Divide[12, 3]**

Out[15]= 4

Instead of the forward slash symbol, the Wolfram Language allows us to create proper fractions. This can be done by selecting the appropriate key in the Basic Math Assistant palette (which is accessible through the **Palettes** menu item). A quick keyboard shortcut is also available. On Windows or Linux computers, enter the numerator and then hit the ctrl key and the forward slash. The fraction bar will appear along with a space for you to enter the denominator. On Mac computers, the key combination used is command and forward slash.

To use a proper fraction, type the number followed by ctrl or command and then forward slash:

In[16]:= $\dfrac{12}{3}$

Out[16]= 4

When the remainder is not zero, the Wolfram Language displays a simplified fraction in keeping with its mathematical roots:

In[17]:= **32/6**

Out[17]= $\dfrac{16}{3}$

If a numerical solution with decimal places is needed, we can use the N function:

In[18]:= **N[32/6]**

Out[18]= 5.33333

Postfix notation (//) dispenses with the normal closed brackets of functions:

In[19]:= **32/6 // N**

Out[19]= 5.33333

There is also the prefix notation using the @ symbol, which is made using shift 2 on most keyboards.

Use of prefix notation removes the need for opening and closing square brackets:

In[20]:= **N@32/6**

Out[20]= 5.33333

The N function also allows us to specify the arbitrary precision:

In[21]:= **N[32/6, 2]**

Out[21]= 5.3

The Round function will round off our answers to the nearest integer. In our example of dividing 6 into 32, we see a value of 5.3333:

In[22]:= **Round[$\dfrac{32}{6}$]**

Out[22]= 5

We can ask for rounding up or down. The Floor function rounds down and the Ceiling function rounds up:

In[23]:= **Floor[32 / 6]**

Out[23]= 5

In[24]:= **Ceiling[$\dfrac{32}{6}$]**

Out[24]= 6

Powers

Likewise, there are a number of ways to use exponents in the Wolfram Language.

The symbol for a power in the Wolfram Language is simply the caret (^):

In[25]:= **10 ^ 4**

Out[25]= 10 000

As with division, we can use the Basic Math Assistant palette or, even easier, the Windows and Mac keyboard shortcut shift 6 . To bring the cursor back to the baseline, simply hit the forward arrow key on your keyboard.

Here is the problem using the shortcut to make a superscript power:

In[26]:= **10^4**

Out[26]= 10 000

The Wolfram Language function that accomplishes this calculation is Power:

In[27]:= **Power[10, 4]**

Out[27]= 10 000

We can view the internal structure and code that the Wolfram Language sees when we write shorthand notation.

We'll take the expression below and use the FullForm function to show us the structure:

$$x^3 + \left(x\left(x + 2\right)\right)^2$$

In[28]:= **FullForm[$x^3 + (x \times (x + 2))^2$]**

Out[28]//FullForm= Plus[Power[x, 3], Times[Power[x, 2], Power[Plus[2, x], 2]]]

A graphical representation of this is available through the use of the TreeForm function:

In[29]:= **TreeForm[x³ + (x × (x+2))²]**

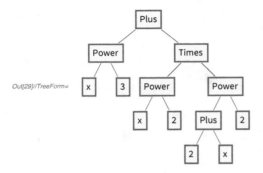

Out[29]//TreeForm=

Logarithmic and Exponential Functions

Transcendental functions such as logarithmic and exponential functions are used in statistical analysis. The logarithmic transform of values (taking the logarithm of each data point value) can be used to transform skewed data point values to a more normal distribution. It is often better to use nonparametric tests, though.

The Log function in the Wolfram Language calculates the natural logarithm of a given numerical value. The natural logarithm is based on Euler's number, *e*. The Log function typically takes two arguments. The first is the base and the second is the value itself. The base value can be omitted. The Wolfram Language will use *e* as the default base value. To return a numerical approximation, we can enter the value in decimal (floating-point) format or use the N function. Without the decimal point, the exact value is returned. The exact solution to the natural logarithm of 1000 is indeed Log[1000] as we see below (or ln(1000) in mathematical, handwritten notation).

Return an exact value:

In[30]:= **Log[1000]**

Out[30]= Log[1000]

Note the use of the decimal version of the numerical value:

In[31]:= **Log[1000.0]**

Out[31]= 6.90776

Use the N function:

In[32]:= **N @ Log[1000]**

Out[32]= 6.90776

For more precision, we can use the N function. The **Log** is placed as first argument and the number of significant digits required is placed as the second argument.

Note that the decimal representation is not required as the N function already returns a numerical approximation:

In[33]:= **N[Log[100 000], 10]**

Out[33]= 11.51292546

The base can be changed by adding a second argument (which is placed first as mentioned).

Calculate the logarithm base-10 of 1000:

In[34]:= **Log[10, 1000]**

Out[34]= 3

The exponent, with Euler's number as base, can be calculated using the **Exp** function. Since any number raised to the power 1 is the number itself, we can check on the value of Euler's number. The N function will return a numerical approximation.

Euler's number with 10 significant digits:

In[35]:= **N[Exp[1], 10]**

Out[35]= 2.718281828

Mathematica is precision software, and that precision can extend as far as your computer's processing power can manage, so use mathematical constants wherever possible to keep that precision high.

Calculate Euler's number exactly with Exp:

In[36]:= **Exp[1]**

Out[36]= e

We can print the character for Euler's number directly in a calculation using the [esc] key method. This is done by hitting [esc], typing the e character on your keyboard twice and hitting the [esc] key again. Below we calculate e^{10}, which is the same as Exp(10).

Use N and the @ shorthand to calculate with Euler's number:

In[37]:= **N @ e^{10}**

Out[37]= 22 026.5

In[38]:= **Exp[10.0]**

Out[38]= 22 026.5

The Order of Execution

The Wolfram Language follows the order of arithmetical execution in the same way you were probably taught in school: parentheses, exponents, multiplication, division, addition, and subtraction.

Calculating the Mean Value

Now that we can do simple arithmetic, let's calculate the mean (or average) of 10 values, 10.0, 11.2, 13.2, 13.1, 9.8, 9.7, 8.9, 10.3, 10.4, and 11.0. The equation for the average is given as:

$$\frac{\sum_{i=1}^{n} x_i}{n} = \frac{x_1 + x_2 + x_3 + x_4 + x_5 + x_6 + x_7 + x_8 + x_9 + x_{10}}{10}$$

Here x_i is each of the 10 values, i.e. x_1 is 10.0, x_2 is 11.2, etc. up until x_n, which, in this case, is the last value in the list, $x_{10} = 11.0$. We divide the summation of all 10 values by the number of values. This requires us to add all the values and divide by the number of values. We force the order of arithmetic execution by placing parentheses around the values to be added prior to division by 10.

In the Wolfram Language, parentheses function the same as they do in ordinary math:

In[39]:= **(10+11.2+13.2+13.1+8.8+9.7+8.9+10.3+10.4+11.0)/10**

Out[39]= 10.66

In later chapters, we will make this calculation a lot easier.

As a sneak peek, the code below executes the Mean function:

In[40]:= **Mean[{10, 11.2, 13.2, 13.1, 8.8, 9.7, 8.9, 10.3, 10.4, 11.0}]**

Out[40]= 10.66

Using the Basic Math Assistant Palette

If you are new to Mathematica, you may have seen the **Palettes** menu item and wondered about it. Mathematica has a variety of preloaded palettes that can assist you with entering input that is more complex than what the average QWERTY keyboard supplies. Many of the hot keys described in this chapter can also be found in the Basic Math Assistant palette. For the most part, the basic tools are self explanatory, selecting ▪/□ will yield two small clickable input boxes that will create your fraction in the form in which you are most familiar.

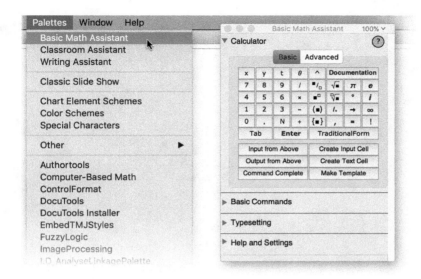

Exercises

Create your own Wolfram Notebook and do the following exercises.

2.1 Add the following numbers using convenience syntax: 1, 4, 14, 14, −3, 2.

2.2 Do the same calculation as in 1 above but use a Wolfram Language function.

2.3 Calculate the following powers:

a. 5 to the power 2

b. 27 to the power $\frac{1}{3}$

c. 10000 to the power $\frac{1}{2}$

2.4 If taking the square root of a number is accomplished using the Sqrt function, calculate the square root of the following numbers:

9, 10000, 2

2.5 If calculating the sine function (to type "π" use (esc) pi (esc)) is accomplished using Sin, calculate the sine of the following numbers (given in radians):

0, $\frac{\pi}{3}$, $\frac{\pi}{2}$

2.6 Calculate the mean of the following data point values: 10, 12, 14, 12, 13, 10, 9, 16.

More to Explore

See Section 1 of *An Elementary Introduction to the Wolfram Language* (wolfr.am/t7cYIi0m)

If you prefer videos, check out the Hands-on Start to Mathematica video series (wolfr.am/t7d2AcBl)

3 | Collections

Now that we have had our first look at the use of the Wolfram Language through simple arithmetical operations, it is time to look at presenting data or at least *lists of numbers*.

This will be very important when we get to analyzing data, as it is most common to have data stored in lists. The Wolfram Language can store many forms of data in lists, and this allows for easy manipulation of the elements (values) contained in lists.

Lists

We have seen how easy it is to do simple arithmetic in the previous chapter. While it is convenient to add values one by one, we might find it more convenient to store quite a few more of them prior to any calculation or action. Collections, or sets of elements, be they numbers or mathematical variables or strings (words and letters), can be stored as lists. Lists can be created in two ways:

1. Using curly braces, {...}, with the elements separated by commas
2. Using the List function, again with the elements separated by commas

Arithmetical operators, such as addition and multiplication, can act on elements in a list. Lists can even be nested, creating a list of lists.

It is common in computer languages to refer to collections or entities, such as lists, as objects. In the case of a list, we will then refer to a list object. For ease of identification of list objects, we will refer to them in uppercase format in the text below, i.e. Lists.

Creating Lists

In the Wolfram Language code that follows, we create our first List. Through the use of the assignment operator (=), we also assign this List (an object containing a list of elements) to a *computer variable*. Such a variable is a space in memory, where our List will be stored for easy retrieval. Within certain limits, we can name this computer variable whatever we wish. The convention is to start with a lowercase letter and indicate separate words by starting each such word with an uppercase letter. Do not use one of the more than 6000 Wolfram Language function names and try to keep the names meaningful. Doing so will allow you to deduce its use when you review your code at a later time or when you share it with others.

In the first example below, the List is stored in the computer variable named myList1. You will note that the List contains a mix of numbers and a word (termed a string). The latter is placed inside of quotation marks, to indicate that it is not the name of a function or variable, but instead a String.

Method 1

Use curly braces to create a computer variable called myList1:

In[1]:= **myList1 = {1, 2, 3, "Mathematica"}**

Out[1]= {1, 2, 3, Mathematica}

The Wolfram Language creates a space in your computer's memory and gives it a name. In this case, we called it myList1. The assignment operator (=) assigns what is on its right-hand side to whatever is on its left-hand side. It is not an equal sign like we might use in formal mathematics.

It is now trivial to retrieve the List by simply referencing the computer variable name. Note how the string (the word "Mathematica" that we placed inside of quotation marks) is displayed without quotation marks.

Retrieve an object from memory by simply referencing and evaluating:

In[2]:= **myList1**

Out[2]= {1, 2, 3, Mathematica}

In the code below, we accomplish the same task using the List function. We assign it to the computer variable name myList2.

Method 2

Use the List function to create the computer variable myList2:

In[3]:= **myList2 = List[1, 2, 3, "Mathematica"]**

Out[3]= {1, 2, 3, Mathematica}

While a single equal sign is the assignment operator, the Wolfram Language also contains the double equal symbol (==), which is the shorthand notation for the Equal function. This is used to test whether two computer variables are equal. This system of checking certain conditions is referred to as Boolean logic. The results are either True or False. It is quite easy to see that myList1 and myList2 contain the same information. Let's test this with the use of the == symbol.

Use Boolean logic to test whether the computer variables myList1 and myList2 are the same:

In[4]:= **myList1 == myList2**

Out[4]= True

Use the Equal function:

In[5]:= **Equal[myList1, myList2]**

Out[5]= True

The Wolfram Langue evaluates this question and indeed returns a True value.

Then there is the shorthand notation triple equal symbol (===). The full function name is SameQ. This Boolean function shorthand checks for both value and type, in as much as 3 is an integer but 3.0 is a decimal value (referred to as a floating-point value). The code below shows the difference between these two functions.

The values 3 and 3.0 are indeed equal:

In[6]:= **3 == 3.0**

Out[6]= True

They are not of the same type, though:

In[7]:= **3 === 3.0**

Out[7]= False

SameQ is the full function name:

In[8]:= **SameQ[3, 3.0]**

Out[8]= False

We need not only test for equality. The != shorthand symbol or the Unequal function checks whether values are dissimilar. The shorthand symbol (=!=) or the function UnsameQ checks for both value and type.

The values 3 and 3.0 are indeed equal, hence a False value is returned:

In[9]:= **3 ≠ 3.0**

Out[9]= False

While the values 3 and 3.0 are equal, they are not of the same type, hence True is returned:

In[10]:= **3 =!= 3.0**

Out[10]= True

Finally, there are the more familiar >, <, ≥, and ≤ symbols (respectively greater than, less than, greater than or equal to, and less than or equal to). Using these is akin to the use of the double equal sign in that a Boolean question is asked. Below we simply check whether the integer 4 is less than the integer 3 (which it obviously is not). In the spoken word, this would be read as, "Is four less than three?"

Check whether 4 is less than 3:

In[11]:= **4 < 3**

Out[11]= False

As expected, we note the return of a False value.

Using Arithmetical Operations on Lists

Arithmetical operators, such as multiplication, can act on the elements in a list. In the first example, we wish to multiply each element in the list by the number (scalar) 2.

Multiply the List by a scalar. Note how the string is seen as mathematical symbol:

In[12]:= **2 ∗ myList1**

Out[12]= {2, 4, 6, 2 Mathematica}

We can add a number (scalar) value to each element in a List. In the next example, the number 3 is added to each element.

Elementwise addition of a scalar to a List:

In[13]:= **3 + myList1**

Out[13]= {4, 5, 6, 3 + Mathematica}

Next, we see an example of pairwise multiplication. Each element is multiplied by its corresponding element in the second List, in the order in which they appear. Note that for this to work, we need the same number of elements in each List. In the output, we note that 1 squared is 1, 2 times 2 is 4, 3 times 3 is 9, and Mathematica times Mathematica is Mathematica^2.

Multiply Lists:

In[14]:= **myList1 ∗ myList2**

Out[14]= {1, 4, 9, Mathematica^2}

Lastly, we see an example where each of the corresponding elements in the two Lists are added to each other. This will only work if, once again, the Lists have the same number of elements in them.

Add Lists:

In[15]:= **myList1 + myList2**

Out[15]= {2, 4, 6, 2 Mathematica}

Nesting Lists

Lists themselves can be elements in a larger List. Below we place both myList1 and myList2 in a List called myList3. Note the use of double curly braces in the output. The computer variable myList3 is indeed a List of Lists.

Make a List of Lists:

In[16]:= **myList3 = {myList1, myList2}**

Out[16]= {{1, 2, 3, Mathematica}, {1, 2, 3, Mathematica}}

Matrices

Matrices consist of rows and columns of elements. They are very useful mathematical objects. We store matrices in the Wolfram Language as nested Lists. In the first example, we recreate the matrix in the expression below, which contains two rows and two columns of numbers.

$$\begin{pmatrix} 1 & 2 \\ 3 & 7 \end{pmatrix}$$

The first row contains the numbers 1 and 2. The second row contains the numbers 3 and 7. The first column then contains the numbers 1 and 3 and the second column contains the numbers 2 and 7. Let's call this nested list myMatrix1.

Create a matrix named myMatrix1:

In[17]:= **myMatrix1 = {{1, 2}, {3, 7}}**

Out[17]= {{1, 2}, {3, 7}}

Note that if we wish to represent a matrix where the entries are done in row-wise fashion, i.e. the first row contained the values 1 and 2, they are entered as the first element in the nested List.

To show this matrix in proper mathematical notation as we did above, we can accomplish this with the MatrixForm function. It can be used in prefix, postfix, or function form.

Using the @ Prefix notation:

In[18]:= **MatrixForm @ myMatrix1**

Out[18]//MatrixForm= $\begin{pmatrix} 1 & 2 \\ 3 & 7 \end{pmatrix}$

Note that no additional spaces are necessary with the postfix notation:

In[19]:= **myMatrix1 // MatrixForm**

Out[19]//MatrixForm= $\begin{pmatrix} 1 & 2 \\ 3 & 7 \end{pmatrix}$

For the purposes of this book, function form is fine:

In[20]:= **MatrixForm[myMatrix1]**

Out[20]//MatrixForm= $\begin{pmatrix} 1 & 2 \\ 3 & 7 \end{pmatrix}$

It is important to note that while we use MatrixForm for visual representation, we should omit it when doing calculations. In the next piece of code, we add the value 3 to each element in our original computer variable myMatrix1.

Add 3 to each element in the matrix:

In[21]:= **myMatrix1 + 3**

Out[21]= **{{4, 5}, {6, 10}}**

List Comprehension

Instead of adding values to a List in manual fashion by typing them in one at a time, we can use an expression (a recipe or a pattern) to create the values. This is done using the very powerful Table function. Doing so is sometimes referred to as List *comprehension*. Until you see it in action a few times, it might appear a little confusing.

As an example then, let's create a list of the first 10 positive integers, that is, 1 through 10. Instead of typing the values, we will use a placeholder name. In the code below, we will use the letter *i*. We do not want to manipulate this placeholder in any way, i.e. multiply it by 2, so we just state it on its own. Then, inside of curly braces, we reference this placeholder and then its *start* and *stop* values and its *step size*. We will start at 1 and go to 10 in steps of 1. This *start-stop-step size* is referred to as the *iterator*.

Create a List of integers starting at 1 and incrementing in steps of 1 to the value 10:

In[22]:= **myTable1 = Table[i, {i, 1, 10, 1}]**

Out[22]= **{1, 2, 3, 4, 5, 6, 7, 8, 9, 10}**

The Wolfram Language makes use of a few defaults for the iterator. If a single value is used, it is assumed that the start is 1 and that the step size is 1.

Omit the start and step size values:

In[23]:= **Table[i, {i, 10}]**

Out[23]= **{1, 2, 3, 4, 5, 6, 7, 8, 9, 10}**

We can also use different start values and step sizes.

Use a different starting value and step size:

In[24]:= **Table[i, {i, 2, 4, 0.2}]**

Out[24]= {2., 2.2, 2.4, 2.6, 2.8, 3., 3.2, 3.4, 3.6, 3.8, 4.}

The Wolfram Language even allows us to go in reverse.

Iterate backward:

In[25]:= **Table[i, {i, 10, 1, −1}]**

Out[25]= {10, 9, 8, 7, 6, 5, 4, 3, 2, 1}

Let's create a second list, going through the values 1 to 5 and squaring each. Our expression now becomes i^2. (Remember that we create the superscript syntax for the square by hitting esc or command and the number 6, or alternatively, we could use the caret ($\wedge$) symbol.)

Use i^2 as the expression to calculate the square of the first five natural numbers:

In[26]:= **myTable2 = Table[i^2, {i, 1, 5, 1}]**

Out[26]= {1, 4, 9, 16, 25}

It can be quite useful to iterate through more than one placeholder. In the Wolfram Language, the iteration starts at the last placeholder. This is done for each of the preceding placeholder values. Next we see an example of iteration through the values 1 to 9 in steps of 4, that is, 1, 5, and 9. This is for the placeholder j. This happens for each of the values in the preceding placeholder, i, which in turn iterates through 1 to 9 in steps of 2, which is 1, 3, 5, 7, and 9. In this example, we add each of the values. Since i starts at 1 and j starts at 1, the first addition will be $1 + 1 = 2$, followed by $1 + 5 = 6$ and $1 + 9 = 10$ as we iterate through all the values of j for the first value of i. Then we move to the next i value and again iterate through all the j values.

Use more than one index to create a nested List:

In[27]:= **myTable3 = Table[i + j, {i, 1, 9, 2}, {j, 1, 9, 4}]**

Out[27]= {{2, 6, 10}, {4, 8, 12}, {6, 10, 14}, {8, 12, 16}, {10, 14, 18}}

The first nested List will be created by $1 + 1$, $1 + 5$, and $1 + 9$ (looping through all the j's for each i loop). The second nested List will be created by $3 + 1$, $3 + 5$, and $3 + 9$.

Practice using the Table function.

Accessing Elements of a List

While it is handy to use list comprehension or even to manually type in large lists, it will inevitably become necessary to reference some of the values. Fortunately, each element in these Lists has an *address*, also called an index value. We can reference these addresses to access specific values. Address referencing in the Wolfram Language is done by the use of a set of double square brackets. Let's have a look again at myList1. Each element in the list has an index (address), starting with the value 1.

Print myList1 to the screen:

In[28]:= **myList1**

Out[28]= {1, 2, 3, Mathematica}

In the next code cell, we recall the computer variable and then put the number 1 inside of double square brackets, indicating the first element in the List, which happens to be 1.

The first element:

In[29]:= **myList1[[1]]**

Out[29]= 1

What about the fourth element?

The fourth element:

In[30]:= **myList1[[4]]**

Out[30]= Mathematica

The Wolfram Language has a more attractive double bracket format as well, sometimes called "operator" form. Simply type the [esc] key before and after each set of brackets, that is, [esc] [[[esc] and [esc]]] [esc].

Use operator notation:

In[31]:= **myList1⟦4⟧**

Out[31]= Mathematica

Sometimes you may need to index the last element in a list. This might be difficult as we do not always know the number of elements in the List. The -1 index allows us to easily index the last element. The Last function also works on lists to grab the last value.

Index the last item in the List:

In[32]:= **myList1⟦−1⟧**

Out[32]= Mathematica

You may wonder what happens to a List of Lists (a matrix) when we use indexing. Let's recall myTable3 and see what happens if we index the first element.

Print myTable3 to the screen:

In[33]:= **myTable3**

Out[33]= {2, 6, 10}, {4, 8, 12}, {6, 10, 14}, {8, 12, 16}, {10, 14, 18}}

View it in matrix form:

In[34]:= **myTable3 // MatrixForm**

Out[34]//MatrixForm=
$$\begin{pmatrix} 2 & 6 & 10 \\ 4 & 8 & 12 \\ 6 & 10 & 14 \\ 8 & 12 & 16 \\ 10 & 14 & 18 \end{pmatrix}$$

Address the first element:

In[35]:= **myTable3[[1]]**

Out[35]= {2, 6, 10}

Note that since it is a List of Lists (each of which we can term a *subList*), we get the first subList back. If we consider this to be part of a matrix, we get the first row back. This is important, since we can reference a certain element by its row and column value. Note that the column value will be the address index within the subList. This row and column indexing is expressed as two values, separated by a comma, so if we want the element in row 1, column 2 (that will be the second element in the first subList), we do the following.

Find the second element in the first subList. If viewed as a matrix, this will be the element in row 1, column 2:

In[36]:= **myTable3[[1, 2]]**

Out[36]= 6

A very useful notation is that of the double semicolon (;;). It basically states that you want all the elements. Imagine then that we want all of the elements in column 3, that is, all of the last elements in each subList.

Get all of the last elements in each subList. If viewed as a matrix, this will be all of the elements in column 3:

In[37]:= **myTable3[[All, 3]]**

Out[37]= {10, 12, 14, 16, 18}

The addressing above states that you want all of the row values in column 3. We can also use the ;; shorthand notation instead of the All function.

Use ;; instead of All:

In[38]:= **myTable3[[;; , 3]]**

Out[38]= {10, 12, 14, 16, 18}

We can also use the double semicolon to specify a range of addresses. Let's ask for the elements 2 through 4 in column 3.

Get the last elements in subLists 2 through 4. If viewed as a matrix, these will be elements 2 through 4 in column 3:

In[39]:= **myTable3[[2 ;; 4, 3]]**

Out[39]= {12, 14, 16}

Now, if we only want elements from rows 2 and 4 in column 3, we need to use curly braces (i.e. a List).

Get the last elements for subLists 2 and 4 only. When viewed as a matrix, this will be elements in rows 2 and 4 for column 3:

In[40]:= **myTable3[[{2, 4}, 3]]**

Out[40]= {12, 16}

The Size of a List

It may be useful to know how many elements there are in a List. For this, we use the Length function. In conjunction with List, it will return the number of elements. In the case of a List of Lists, it will return the number of subLists.

Recall myList1:

In[41]:= **myList1**

Out[41]= {1, 2, 3, Mathematica}

Calculate the number of elements in myList1:

In[42]:= **Length[myList1]**

Out[42]= 4

In the next example, we take a look at the nested List myTable3.

Recall myTable3 and find the number of subLists:

In[43]:= **myTable3**

Out[43]= {{2, 6, 10}, {4, 8, 12}, {6, 10, 14}, {8, 12, 16}, {10, 14, 18}}

In[44]:= **Length[myTable3]**

Out[44]= 5

We note that it returns the number of subLists as we expected.

Let's see what happens if we have a deeper nesting. In the example below, we have a List containing five subLists, which in turn each contain two subLists, which in turn each contain two elements. We'll use the Length function and check the result.

Create a deeply nested List:

In[45]:= **myList4 = {{{1, 2}, {1, 3}}, {{3, 4}, {2, 5}}, {{0, 1}, {3, 3}}, {{2, 0}, {1, 2}}, {{4, 2}, {4, 1}}}**

Out[45]= {{{1, 2}, {1, 3}}, {{3, 4}, {2, 5}}, {{0, 1}, {3, 3}}, {{2, 0}, {1, 2}}, {{4, 2}, {4, 1}}}

The length of the deeply nested List:

In[46]:= **Length[myList4]**

Out[46]= 5

The matrix form is seen in the output below.

The matrix form of a deeply nested list, is also called a tensor:

In[47]:= **MatrixForm @ myList4**

$$
Out[47]//MatrixForm= \begin{pmatrix} \begin{pmatrix} 1 \\ 2 \end{pmatrix} & \begin{pmatrix} 1 \\ 3 \end{pmatrix} \\ \begin{pmatrix} 3 \\ 4 \end{pmatrix} & \begin{pmatrix} 2 \\ 5 \end{pmatrix} \\ \begin{pmatrix} 0 \\ 1 \end{pmatrix} & \begin{pmatrix} 3 \\ 3 \end{pmatrix} \\ \begin{pmatrix} 2 \\ 0 \end{pmatrix} & \begin{pmatrix} 1 \\ 2 \end{pmatrix} \\ \begin{pmatrix} 4 \\ 2 \end{pmatrix} & \begin{pmatrix} 4 \\ 1 \end{pmatrix} \end{pmatrix}
$$

We note that it is the number of first-level subLists that is returned when using the Length function. We can always use addressing to get to elements we want. In the example, we ask for the value of the second element in the second nested List of the first nested List, which is 3.

Address a deeply nested List:

In[48]:= **myList4⟦1, 2, 2⟧**

Out[48]= 3

To get the total number of elements in a list, we can use the **Flatten** function to create a non-nested List. This removes all the elements from the subLists and places them in a single List, the elements of which we can then count. In order to do this, we nest the Wolfram Language functions, that is **Length[Flatten[]]**.

Flatten the nested List:

In[49]:= **Flatten[myList4]**

Out[49]= {1, 2, 1, 3, 3, 4, 2, 5, 0, 1, 3, 3, 2, 0, 1, 2, 4, 2, 4, 1}

The List is flattened with the use of the **Flatten** function and the elements are then counted using the **Length** function.

Count the number of elements by nesting the Wolfram Language functions:

In[50]:= **Length[Flatten[myList4]]**

Out[50]= 20

Appending Elements to a List

We can add elements to a List using the **Append** function. In the example below, we revisit **myList1** and add the string (text) "This is great!" to it. The **Append** function takes the computer variable (object) as first argument, followed by the element (number, list, or string) that should be appended to the end.

The original myList1:

In[51]:= **myList1**

Out[51]= {1, 2, 3, Mathematica}

Append the string to myList1:

In[52]:= **Append[myList1, "This is great!"]**

Out[52]= {1, 2, 3, Mathematica, This is great!}

Note, though, that if we call **myList1** again, the appended string is not there:

In[53]:= **myList1**

Out[53]= {1, 2, 3, Mathematica}

We can make this change permanent during our current session by using the AppendTo function.

Use the AppendTo function to make a permanent addition:

In[54]:= **AppendTo[myList1, "This is great!"]**

Out[54]= {1, 2, 3, Mathematica, This is great!}

In[55]:= **myList1**

Out[55]= {1, 2, 3, Mathematica, This is great!}

As mentioned, this permanency only refers to our current session. Once we close Mathematica or restart the Wolfram Language kernel, all the information inside of our computer variables, and indeed the computer variable names themselves, are lost. We have to re-execute each cell to reinstate them.

There is another way to append elements to a List, and it uses assignment. It is actually important to take a closer look at this example involving assignment. As mentioned in the prior Lists, = assigns whatever is on the right-hand side of it to whatever is on the left-hand side of it. In this incarnation, it is most unlike our mathematical sense of the equal sign, which equates and does not assign.

In the next example, we create a computer variable called x and assign to it the number 5.

Assign the integer value 5 to the computer variable x:

In[56]:= **x = 5**

Out[56]= 5

This is an assignment. The computer variable x holds an integer object with the value 5. This was assigned to the computer variable by the equal sign. Watch now as we assign a new value to the computer variable, using its previously held value.

Add 1 to the value currently held in the computer variable x:

In[57]:= **x = x + 1**

Out[57]= 6

Algebraically, this makes no sense. If we try and solve for x as a mathematical variable we get $0 = 1$. On the right-hand side we see $x + 1$. As it stands, the computer variable x holds the value 5. We then add 1 to it, resulting in the value 6. This new value is now assigned to the computer variable x. The value 5, which it held, is now replaced or overwritten by the value 6.

Instead of using the AppendTo function, we can use a similar principle. We'll recreate myList1 and then permanently append our string to the end of it.

Recreate the myList1 computer variable:

In[58]:= **myList1 = {1, 2, 3, "Mathematica"}**

Out[58]= {1, 2, 3, Mathematica}

Use assignment to append to this List by overwriting it:

In[59]:= **myList1 = Append[myList1, "This is great!"]**

Out[59]= {1, 2, 3, Mathematica, This is great!}

Check to see of the change was permanent:

In[60]:= **myList1**

Out[60]= {1, 2, 3, Mathematica, This is great!}

Selecting Items from a List

While it is useful to store elements in a List and to select certain values using an index or addressing system, it is much more useful to select elements from a List based on some criteria. Imagine then for a moment that we have a List stored in a computer variable. This list holds the values for some laboratory measurements taken during an experiment. We'll call it myVariable and add some values to it manually.

Creating a List of 20 measurements taken during our experiment:

In[61]:= **myVariable = {15.4, 12.3, 16.3, 15.0, 20.1, 19, 8, 15.2,**
       16.5, 15.0, 18.3, 14.3, 9.8, 2.1, 18.3, 17.2, 15.5, 25.9, 14.9, 20.1}

Out[61]= {15.4, 12.3, 16.3, 15., 20.1, 19, 8, 15.2, 16.5,
       15., 18.3, 14.3, 9.8, 2.1, 18.3, 17.2, 15.5, 25.9, 14.9, 20.1}

Suppose now that we only want to work on values that are greater than or equal to 18. This is quite easy to accomplish using the Select function. The first argument holds the List name (the computer variable name holding the list object) followed by the criteria we wish to set. The Wolfram Language uses the pound or hash sign (#) as a placeholder for each element in the List. The greater than or equal to sign is typed as ⌜esc⌝ >= ⌜esc⌝. Always remember the & sign that follows the criteria.

Select all the values greater than or equal to 18. The ≥ sign asks a Boolean question, so the number is returned only when a true value is found:

In[62]:= **Select[myVariable, # ≥ 18 &]**

Out[62]= {20.1, 19, 18.3, 18.3, 25.9, 20.1}

All of the values that show up are now greater than or equal to 18.

We can do the same with string values. Below we create a List of genus and species names and assign it to the computer variable myOrganisms.

Creating a list of string values:

In[63]:= **myOrganisms = {"Staphylococcus aureus", "Proteus mirabilis",**
"Acinetobacter baumanii", "Eschericia coli", "Klebsiella pneumoniae",
"Proteus mirabilis", "Streptococcus pyogenes", "Staphylococcus aureus",
"Proteus mirabilis", "Acinetobacter baumanii", "Eschericia coli",
"Klebsiella pneumoniae", "Streptococcus pyogenes",
"Acinetobacter baumanii", "Eschericia coli", "Proteus mirabilis"}

Out[63]= {Staphylococcus aureus, Proteus mirabilis, Acinetobacter baumanii,
Eschericia coli, Klebsiella pneumoniae, Proteus mirabilis, Streptococcus pyogenes,
Staphylococcus aureus, Proteus mirabilis, Acinetobacter baumanii,
Eschericia coli, Klebsiella pneumoniae, Streptococcus pyogenes,
Acinetobacter baumanii, Eschericia coli, Proteus mirabilis}

We may only want to work with a single species. We use the Select function and assign the result to a new computer variable.

Use the Select function and == to get a single species:

In[64]:= **myImportantOrganism = Select[myOrganisms, # == "Acinetobacter baumanii" &]**

Out[64]= {Acinetobacter baumanii, Acinetobacter baumanii, Acinetobacter baumanii}

This example was a bit trivial. In later chapters, we will have multiple variables nested as a List of Lists. We will use the matrix view, making our data appear as a spreadsheet. Every column holds the values for a variable. If we extract only a single organism as in the previous example, we will also extract only its corresponding values in the other columns.

Lastly, it may be useful to extract the index value for the criteria that we set. In the next example, we use the Position function to see what positions (index values) the *Acinetobacter baumanii* organism held.

The index values:

In[65]:= **Position[myOrganisms, "Acinetobacter baumanii"]**

Out[65]= {{3}, {10}, {14}}

We see that it was listed as elements 3, 10, and 14.

That's it for the List function. As we start doing some real statistics and data analysis, we will see a lot of data stored in Lists and nested Lists.

Exercises

3.1 Create a list with the following elements: 1, 2, 3, 4. Store the List in the computer variable myList1.

3.2 Repeat the process in problem 1 for the elements 10, 11, 12, 13 and store it in the computer variable myList2.

3.3 Add myList1 and myList2.

3.4 Multiply the elements of myList1 and myList2.

3.5 Use the Table function to create a list of the cubes of the integers 1 through 7. Save the created list to the computer variable myCubes.

3.6 Use [[...]] addressing to extract the fifth element of myCubes.

3.7 Use the Table function to add two values, *i* and *j*, with *i* iterating through the values 1, 2, 3, 4, 5 and *j* iterating through 1, 2. Save the resulting nested list in the computer variable myPairs.

3.8 Express myPairs in matrix format.

3.9 Use [[...]] addressing to display only the values in the last column of problem 8, myPairs, i.e. all the rows in column 2.

3.10 Use the Table function to create a list of the first 10 even numbers, i.e. 2, 4, 6, 8, 10, 12, 14, 16, 18, 20. Save the List object in the computer variable myEvens.

3.11 Use the Select function to select only values that are less than 10 from myEvens.

3.12 Transform myEvens with the next 10 even numbers and flatten to a single List.

More to Explore

For a list of other functions used with List manipulation, try this guide from the Wolfram Language & System Documentation Center (wolfr.am/APH24IBF)

More things you can do with, and to, Lists are explained in Section 5 of Stephen Wolfram's *An Elementary Introduction to the Wolfram Language* (wolfr.am/eiwl-5)

4 | Working with Datasets

Now that we are familiar with List objects, we can transfer this knowledge to something closer to the real-world data that we use in statistics and data analysis. In this chapter, we work with a kind of List object called a Dataset object.

You will see that it looks very much like a spreadsheet file. Although there are other use cases for Dataset objects, it is perhaps most common to use them in the setting of importing spreadsheet files. In a spreadsheet, we have rows of data across one or more columns. Typically, each row represents data from a single sample subject. Across the columns we will have the numerous variables for which we collect data point values for each subject.

Other than importing spreadsheets as Dataset objects, we can also create them from scratch. This requires understanding associations and is exactly what we will start with.

Creating a Dataset

A Dataset object is similar to a nested List object but with a few extra features. Formally, it represents structured data that is based on a hierarchy of lists and associations. An example or two will clarify this structure.

Associations contain *key-value pairs*. A key-value pair consists of a value (the value part of the pair) and a name for that value (the key part of the pair). Below we see a value of 100 with the key called "weight."

Create an Association:

```
In[1]:= Association["weight" → 200]

Out[1]= <| weight → 200 |>
```

Note the special syntax of the output, using the <, |, and > symbols. Let's expand on this idea of an association with a set of weight and height key-value pairs across multiple examples.

The output here is not important and usually would be suppressed using the ; shorthand as part of your code:

```
In[2]:= subjectOne = Association["weight" → 200, "height" → 72, "age" → 33]
        subjectTwo = Association["weight" → 180, "height" → 80, "age" → 34]
        subjectThree = Association["weight" → 170, "height" → 70, "age" → 53]
        subjectFour = Association["weight" → 180, "height" → 72, "age" → 22]
        subjectFive = Association["weight" → 150, "height" → 55, "age" → 61]
```

Out[2]= <| weight → 200, height → 72, age → 33 |>

Out[3]= <| weight → 180, height → 80, age → 34 |>

Out[4]= <| weight → 170, height → 70, age → 53 |>

Out[5]= <| weight → 180, height → 72, age → 22 |>

Out[6]= <| weight → 150, height → 55, age → 61 |>

We can combine the Association objects into a Dataset object. Dataset objects can be created manually using the Dataset function. In the first example, we create a Dataset object called **dataset**. As a reminder, note our convention of using a lowercase first letter in our computer variable name. This clearly identifies it as a name of our choice in contrast to Wolfram Language functions that always start with an uppercase letter. Our Dataset object combines the five Association objects we created as a List object.

Manually create a Dataset object:

```
In[7]:= dataset = Dataset[{subjectOne, subjectTwo, subjectThree, subjectFour, subjectFive}]
```

Out[7]=

weight	height	age
200	72	33
180	80	34
170	70	53
180	72	22
150	55	61

In this representation, it does indeed look like a spreadsheet file, with three columns of variables and with five rows of data representing five samples in our research. For each sample, three data point values were collected, one for each of the variables weight, height, and age. We will explore some of the shared properties of our Dataset object with a few demonstrations of nested List objects in the next section.

Referencing Sections of a Dataset

Up until now, we have only worked with List and nested List objects. Let's move on to the data structure we created at the start of this chapter. As mentioned, it shares some of the properties of List objects that are familiar to us. One of these properties is addressing, also called indexing.

Indexing of a Dataset object makes use of the same double square bracket notation ([[...]]) as List objects. In the code, we index only the first row.

Select the first row:

In[8]:= **dataset[[1]]**

	weight	200
Out[8]=	height	72
	age	33

Be careful. When asking only for a single row, the Wolfram Language transposes the output to the screen and the first row of data point values is returned in column form. This is just for ease of viewing and does not change the underlying function or values.

We can also use the *row, column syntax* and use the All function to include all of the columns for row 1.

Do the same as previously but specify that all of the columns should be included:

In[9]:= **dataset[[1, All]]**

	weight	200
Out[9]=	height	72
	age	33

Switching things around, let's select all the row entries from column 1.

Select all of the row entries in the first column:

In[10]:= **dataset[[All, 1]]**

	200
	180
Out[10]=	170
	180
	150

Remember that we can also use the double semicolon notation (;;) to indicate all, or a contiguous selection.

Use double semicolons to indicate all:

In[11]:= **dataset[[;; , 1]]**

Out[11]=

200
180
170
180
150

Use double semicolons to indicate a range and select rows 2 through 5 in column 1:

In[12]:= **dataset[[2 ;; 5, 1]]**

Out[12]=

180
170
180
150

What if we don't want rows 2 and 4 in our selection above? If we want to include only rows 3 and 5, we have to place them in curly braces (creating a List object of the rows that we want).

Select only rows 3 and 5 of the last column:

In[13]:= **dataset[[{3, 5}, 3]]**

Out[13]=

53
61

What about a shorthand way to skip all of the columns except for the last one? This occurs commonly in large Dataset objects where we are unsure as to how many columns (or rows) there are.

To get the last column, we use the shorthand syntax −1:

In[14]:= **dataset[[{3, 5}, −1]]**

Out[14]=

53
61

Many spreadsheet files will have column names (typically stored in the very first row). In our example Dataset object, the values are weight, height, and age, so instead of using the numerical address values, we could use the actual column name as a string when referencing the required column.

Specify all of the rows for the column named "age" instead of the number 3:

In[15]:= **dataset[[All, "age"]]**

Out[15]=

33
34
53
22
61

As you can see, indexing works much as it did with List and nested List objects. It makes for a very powerful way of working with data.

Selecting Rows Based on Conditions

Another property, similar to List objects, that is shared by Dataset objects is the use of conditions. We can specify a condition with which data point values are selected. The Select function allows us to create a conditional *recipe* for this selection. In the first example, we look for all data point values in the weight column that are larger than 170. We follow this up by looking only for rows where the entry in the height column is 72.

Select only the rows in which the value in the weight column is larger than 170:

In[16]:= **dataset[Select[#weight > 170 &]]**

Out[16]=

weight	height	age
200	72	33
180	80	34
180	72	22

Note the use of the placeholder syntax # and the pure function symbol & and that all of the rows that meet the criteria for the weight column are returned.

Select all of the rows for which the data point value in the weight column is 72:

In[17]:= **dataset[Select[*#height* == 72 &]]**

	weight	height	age
Out[17]=	200	72	33
	180	72	22

Note that we use double equal signs (==) instead of a single equal sign because this is a Boolean question and == is used to test equality. On the other hand, = is used to assign a name to something, like we did earlier in the chapter to assign the name "dataset" to our imported data.

We can make our selection conditions very complicated. Let's return only the values in the weight and age columns for which the value in the height column is equal to 72.

Show only the weight and age columns for which the value in the height column is 72:

In[18]:= **dataset[Select[*#height* == 72 &], {"weight", "age"}]**

	weight	age
Out[18]=	200	33
	180	22

When analyzing data, this selection by conditions will allow us to conduct our statistical tests as we group relevant data together.

Calling a Function Using a Dataset Object

Although we take a thorough look at descriptive statistics in Chapter 6, it is worthwhile to take a brief glimpse at an important difference between dealing with a List object and a Dataset object. We will do so by way of calculating the mean of a set of values and also counting the number of elements.

When dealing with a List object, we can simply use the Mean function. Similarly, we can count the number of elements in a List object by using the Length function. Let's create a short List object of numbers and review the syntax.

Create a List object containing numbers:

In[19]:= **shortList = {10.1, 13, 4, 12, 12.4, 15.3, 17.9, 15.5, 13.1, 14, 16.8}**

Out[19]= {10.1, 13, 4, 12, 12.4, 15.3, 17.9, 15.5, 13.1, 14, 16.8}

Calculate the mean of the values:

In[20]:= **Mean[shortList]**

Out[20]= 13.1

Count the number of values:

In[21]:= **Length[shortList]**

Out[21]= 11

When the values are part of a column in a Dataset object, we refer to the Dataset object by name first, pass the required function as an argument, and then pass the column number (or name). In the code below, we will calculate the mean of the values of the weight column.

Find the average of the values in the weight column using postfix notation to return a decimal value:

In[22]:= **dataset[Mean, "weight"] // N**

Out[22]= 176.

To calculate the mean, we obviously required a list of all the values, which are summed and then divided by the number of elements. We might have other reasons to extract all the values in a column. To do this, we can follow a similar syntax to the previous one.

Instead of using the Mean function, we use the List function:

In[23]:= **dataset[List, "weight"]**

Out[23]=

200	180	170	180	150

This returns a Dataset object. Use the Head function to confirm this for yourself. Normal converts a variety of specialized structures into something more easily manipulated using non-specialized Wolfram Language commands. Check the Tech Notes at the end of this chapter for a list of all objects that Normal converts.

To return a List object, we use the Normal function:

In[24]:= **Normal[dataset[List, "weight"]]**

Out[24]= {{200, 180, 170, 180, 150}}

If you look carefully, the Normal function actually returned a nested List object. We simply have to use the index of the single nested list to get a non-nested List object.

You see how Normal flattens the dataset into a simple list:

In[25]:= **Normal[dataset[List, "weight"]]⟦1⟧**

Out[25]= {200, 180, 170, 180, 150}

As a shorter alternative (not requiring extraction of the only element in the returned nested List), we can use the Normal function and indexing of the Dataset object.

All, as in indexer, specifies all parts of a particular level of data:

In[26]:= **Normal[dataset⟦All, "weight"⟧]**

Out[26]= {200, 180, 170, 180, 150}

Lastly, we look at the shape of a Dataset object. This is achieved using the Dimensions function. It returns the number of rows and the number of columns. (Remember that we are actually dealing with associations, but as stated initially, we will use the spreadsheet view of this object most commonly in statistical analysis.) With our Dataset object as argument, it will return the values 5 and 3 to indicate that there are five rows and three columns.

Calculate the number of rows and columns in a dataset:

In[27]:= **Dimensions[dataset]**

Out[27]= {5, 3}

Dividing a Dataset Object by Grouping

One of the powerful properties of a Dataset object is the ability to create groups of data. In the next example, we manually create a new Dataset object called subjects that we will use to illustrate this concept.

Create a Dataset object called subjects:

In[28]:= **subjects = Dataset[{**
        <|"a" → 1, "b" → "x", "c" → 1|>,
        <|"a" → 2, "b" → "y", "c" → 2|>,
        <|"a" → 3, "b" → "z", "c" → 2|>,
        <|"a" → 4, "b" → "x", "c" → 3|>,
        <|"a" → 5, "b" → "y", "c" → 5|>,
        <|"a" → 6, "b" → "z", "c" → 3|>}]

Out[28]=

a	b	c
1	x	1
2	y	2
3	z	2
4	x	3
5	y	5
6	z	3

Column b in our Dataset object has the values x, y, and z. We note specifically that there are two instances each of x, y, and z in this column. It might be very useful to us to group these subjects (rows) together. For instance, we can group the Dataset object so that all of the rows with each of these three unique elements are combined in some way. We could then calculate the mean (or other statistic) of the corresponding values in column c by this grouping.

Calculate the mean of values in column c for each of the unique values in column b:

In[29]:= **subjects[GroupBy["b"], Mean, "c"]**

Out[29]=

x	2
y	7/2
z	5/2

We can see the mean for the values in column c, for which the corresponding values in column b are x, y, and z, respectively.

Creating a sub-Dataset and List Objects

It might be prudent to split a dataset up into smaller Dataset objects. Let's create a new Dataset object from our **subjects** object, where all the rows contain only an x in column b.

Next, we create such a sub-Dataset object and call it **xSubjects**. We do this by use of the Select function as an argument. From the example, we can see why it is important not to have illegal characters in column names (such as spaces). Fortunately, our small dataset has column headers that are a single character each.

Create a sub-Dataset object using the Select function:

In[30]:= **xSubjects = subjects[Select[#b == "x" &]]**

Out[30]=

a	b	c
1	x	1
4	x	3

If we use the Counts function on the **xSubjects** column b, we will see only x values, of which there are two.

Count the categorical data point values in column b:

In[31]:= **xSubjects[Counts, "b"]**

Out[31]=

x	2

To make it easier to use Wolfram Language functions, we can make use of the extracted List objects that we saw in the earlier section "Calling a Function Using a Dataset Object." This will allow us to use the proper syntax, such as Mean[*List_object*] instead of dataset[Mean, "Variable"].

As before, we will use the Normal function. In the next example, we extract only the values in column *c* of our Dataset object and call this List object c.

This method creates a List object in a List object; therefore, we have to specify the first element:

In[32]:= **c = Normal[subjects⟦All, "c"⟧]**

Out[32]= {1, 2, 2, 3, 5, 3}

Just to make sure that we do indeed have a List object, we can use the Head function. We can also now simply use the Mean function with the List object as an argument instead of referencing the Dataset object as we have seen above.

Use the Head function to look at what type of object c is:

In[33]:= **Head[c]**

Out[33]= List

Now use the postfix form of the N function to return a numerical value:

In[34]:= **subjects[Mean, "c"] // N**

Out[34]= 2.66667

Just as an exercise, we end this chapter with a look at how we would accomplish the same task, but on the Dataset object itself, i.e. the mean of the values in column *c*.

Reference column *c* directly:

In[35]:= **dataset[Mean, "c"] // N**

Out[35]= 2.66667

Exercises

4.1 Create a dataset with the following code:
dataset = Dataset[{
<|"a" → 1, "b" → "I", "c" → 2|>,
<|"a" → 2, "b" → "II", "c" → 3|>,
<|"a" → 3, "b" → "II", "c" → 1|>,
<|"a" → 4, "b" → "I", "c" → 1|>,
<|"a" → 5, "b" → "II", "c" → 4|>,
<|"a" → 6, "b" → "I", "c" → 2|>,
<|"a" → 7, "b" → "II", "c" → 5|>,
<|"a" → 8, "b" → "II", "c" → 6|>,
<|"a" → 9, "b" → "I", "c" → 3|>,
<|"a" → 10, "b" → "I", "c" → 2|>,
<|"a" → 11, "b" → "II", "c" → 1|>,
<|"a" → 12, "b" → "I", "c" → 5|>,
<|"a" → 13, "b" → "II", "c" → 5|>}

4.2 How many rows and columns are there in the dataset? (Hint: use the **Dimensions** function.)

4.3 Use [[...]] to show only the values in column *b*.

4.4 Select only rows for which the value in column *c* is equal to or larger than 4.

4.5 Select the values in rows 2 through 4 for columns *b* and *c*.

4.6 Select the values in rows 2 and 4 for columns *a* and *c*.

4.7 Calculate the mean value for the values in column *c*. Express the answer in numeric form.

4.8 Create a list of the values in column *c* and store the list object in the computer variable **variableC**.

Tech Notes

- Possible heads h and h_i in Normal [*expr*, h] and Normal [*expr*, $\{h_1, h_2, ...\}$] are converted as follows:

Association	list of rules
Column	ordinary list
ConditionalExpression	expression in the first argument
Dataset	lists and associations
Dispatch	list of rules
FittedModel	best fit function
GraphicsComplex	ordinary lists of graphics primitives and directives
Grid	list of lists
Quantity (**purely numeric units**)	numbers
RootSum	explicit sums of **Root** objects

Row	ordinary list
Series **or** SeriesData	expression with higher—order terms truncated
SparseArray	ordinary array
StructuredArray	ordinary array
QuantityArray, SymmetrizedArray	ordinary array
TemporalData	ordinary array of time—value pairs
TimeSeriesModel	underlying time series process

More to Explore

As usual, check out the chapter on datasets in *An Elementary Introduction to the Wolfram Language* (wolfr.am/45-datasets)

For some interactive, fun fitting of datasets to models, check out this Wolfram Demonstration by S. Chandler (wolfr.am/MaximumLikelihood)

5 | Data Types

In this chapter, we start our journey into proper statistics and data analysis. The journey begins by classifying data point values as specific types. The ability to do this underlies an important decision: *what statistical test to use when analysing data*. Without knowing what type of data each variable represents, we cannot make this decision.

We will also expand on our knowledge of Dataset objects by importing an actual data file in the form of a spreadsheet. The file used in this text consists of simulated health-care data and does not contain any data on actual people.

Data

Measurements taken during an experiment are termed data point values. Each data point value belongs to a variable. Some examples of variables are length, age, species, luminosity, distance, concentration, price, and choice in a survey question. These are represented as columns in a data file. For each subject in a research project, we will have data point values entered for each of these variables, represented as a row in a data file.

In the previous chapter, we took a look at how a Dataset object is created. While creating our own data can be useful, it is much more common to have data already entered into a data file. In the code on the next page, we import a spreadsheet file from a simulated research project. The import will create a Dataset object similar to the one we created manually. Spreadsheets and other files that we may wish to import with the Wolfram Language can reside anywhere on your hard drive or even on the internet. In many cases, it is good practice to have the data file located in the same folder (directory) as the Wolfram Language file (notebook) in which we are working. This negates the need to type in a long path to the file in question. This is the convention used in this text. Once a notebook is saved locally, we can use the NotebookDirectory function to print the folder (directory) name in which it is stored to the screen.

Print the notebook directory to the screen:

In[1]:= **NotebookDirectory[]**

Out[1]= C:\Users\juank\OneDrive\Mathematica\My books\
Introduction–to–Statistics–with–WolframLanguage\

We need to go one step further and set the current folder (directory) that contains our notebook and data files as the active folder (directory). This is accomplished with the SetDirectory function. We pass the NotebookDirectory function as an argument.

Set the active working directory:

In[2]:= **SetDirectory[NotebookDirectory[]]**

Out[2]= C:\Users\juank\OneDrive\Mathematica\My books\
Introduction–to–Statistics–with–WolframLanguage\

When we now import a file, we do not need to type its complete path (address) on our system drive. Setting the active folder is not strictly necessary. The Wolfram Language makes it easy to browse for a file on your local system by opening a **File Browser** button as soon as you start to enter the argument for the SemanticImport function.

Clicking the button will open your system's drive browser and you can navigate to the file:

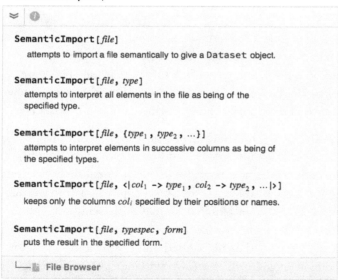

The following code imports a comma-separated value (.csv), spreadsheet file. These files can be created in common spreadsheet software. While most of the programs save the spreadsheet file in a proprietary format, such as .xlsx in the case of Microsoft Excel, they all provide the ability to choose the .csv file format when saving. We use the SemanticImport function and pass the file name and extension as a string inside of quotation marks. We will store this imported spreadsheet in the computer variable called **data**.

We can now omit the complete path to the file. The semicolon suppresses the output:

In[3]:= **data = SemanticImport["Variables.csv"];**

As we noted in the previous chapter, we can use the Head function to look at the object type that was created when we imported the spreadsheet file.

Look at what type of object was stored in the computer variable **data** when we imported the .csv spreadsheet file:

In[4]:= **Head[data]**

Out[4]= Dataset

While you can open the data file in your favorite spreadsheet program, we can also take a look at it right in the notebook using the indexing syntax, with which we are now very familiar. Let's look at the first five rows.

View the first five rows:

In[5]:= **data[[;; 5]]**

Age	Logistics	Temp
77	Immediate Surgical intervention(then Ward / ICU / HCU)	37.4
64	Admit to Ward for Care	38.0
87	Admit to Ward for Care	38.5
70	Admit to Ward for Care	38.2
85	Admit to Ward for Care	38.1

Out[5]= (to the left of the table)

Most datasets are too large to view comfortably at once, and so it is useful to find their dimensions.

Determine the number of rows and columns in the Dataset object:

In[6]:= **Dimensions[data]**

Out[6]= {597, 8}

Note that there are 597 rows of data representing the data point values collected for 597 subjects and that these data point values represent eight variables.

The column headers are each appropriately named for a variable. We have *Age*, *Logistics*, *Temp*, *InsulinDependentDiabetic*, *HB*, *TreatmentGroup*, *SurveyQuestion1*, and *Improvement*. You will note that there are no spaces or other special characters in the variable names. This was done intentionally when the spreadsheet file was created and makes it easier when we write Wolfram Language code for analysis. It is a good idea to save the names in a similar format when collecting data.

Each row, then, represents the data point values for each of the variables entered for a particular participant in the research project. We can take a look at the first row of the object to familiarize ourselves with the data. The first participant is 77 years of age, was immediately operated on, had a temperature of 37.4 degrees Celsius, did not have insulin-dependent diabetes mellitus, had an HB value of 9.2, fell in treatment group I, answered the value 5 for the first question on a survey given to all partici-pants, and showed zero improvement (more on this last column later). We can print this to the screen. Remember that the Wolfram Language will transpose this single row view into column format for display purposes.

Look at the first row of data:

In[7]:= **data⟦1⟧**

Out[7]=

Age	77
Logistics	Immediate Surgical intervention(then Ward / ICU / HCU)
Temp	37.4
InsulinDependentDiabetic	No
SurveyQuestion1	5

This row versus column format is ideal for working with data and analyzing it using the Wolfram Language. For the sake of clarity, we will keep to the term *variable* and call each entry a *data point value*.

You will notice that all the data point values for the *Age* variable are integer values. The data point values for the *Logistics* variable are words (strings). There are only a few unique ones, though, such as *Admit to Ward for Care* and *Immediate Surgical intervention (then Ward/ICU/HCU)*. We can all agree that numbers and words are different types of data.

If we have words (strings) as data point values, we can count the number of each specific entry. The Counts function will count the number of unique entries found in the specified column, regardless of text or value.

Count the number of unique entries found in the *Logistics* column:

In[8]:= **data[Counts, "Logistics"]**

Out[8]=

Immediate Surgical intervention(then Ward / ICU / HCU)	98
Admit to Ward for Care	362
Admit to ICU / HCU for Care	26
Consultation only (leave in original ward)	111

In this instance, we note that there are four unique data point values for the *Logistics* variable, and we can see how many times each occurs in the Dataset object. This is referred to as the frequency of each unique data point value.

The sample space of the variable is a set of all possible values within that variable. The sample space for *Age*, for instance, will be integer values between and including the minimum and maximum values. The specific age value for each subject is drawn from that sample space. In this case, for our data, age is represented as whole numbers above 0.

Pass two functions to the **data** computer variable:

In[9]:= **data[{Min, Max}, "Age"]**

Out[9]= 18 | 90

This code expresses the minimum (Min) and maximum (Max) values for the *Age* column.

The important thing to note in the code above is the fact that the type of data point values that exist for a variable are different. The *Logistics* column has strings (called categories) in its sample space and the *Age* column has integers (called numerical values) in its sample space.

Data Types

As mentioned, you will have noticed that all of the data point values for a variable are similar. We had words and numbers. Each of these have a type name. This allows us a classification system for variables. Our example of integers and strings allows us our first classification of data types, namely *numerical* and *categorical* data types.

Numerical Data Types

As the term implies, a numerical data type consists of numbers. If we consider the *Age* variable, its data point values are indeed numbers and the variable can be classified as numerical.

Here is another example of a numerical variable that shows the minimum and maximum temperature values:

In[10]:= **data[{Min, Max}, "Temp"]**

Out[10]= 35.8 | 39.9

The *Temp* variable is also numerical, but there is a difference, though. Consider the age value of zero. It certainly exists and refers to birth or the first year of life. A patient who is 40 years old is twice as old as one who is 20 years old. The same cannot be said for a temperature measured in degrees Celsius or Fahrenheit. Neither contain a true zero. We might say that it is 0°C or 0°F outside, but true zero only exists for the Kelvin scale.

Whereas an age of zero refers to the absence of age, a temperature of 0°C or 0°F does not infer the absence of temperature. This means that we cannot say that a temperature of 80°C is twice as warm as 40°F.

Temperature is therefore classified as *interval-type* numerical data and age would be an example of *ratio-type* numerical data. The majority of numerical data types that you will come across will be ratio-type, and it is common to simply refer to the term *numerical data* when dealing with numbers.

Categorical Data Types

The *Logistics* variable is an example of a categorical data type. The data point values are words. Note also that we cannot put these in any proper order. Think of variables such as *Organism*, *Breed (of Animal)*, *Soil Type*, etc., for which the data point values are drawn from a sample space that is usually expressed as words or characters. Other than by some form of mental interpretation, we cannot put the data point values for these variables in an order as we can do with numbers. We might order them alphabetically, by size of the breed, or by other means, but for statistical purposes, they cannot be ordered. The term for this data type is *nominal* categorical.

The *Improvement* column's data point values are commonly seen in data files, where categorical variables as expressed as numbers. Researchers may choose to enter numbers as placeholders for actual data point values. In this example, 0 might refer to *no improvement* and 1 might refer to *improvement*. It is important to know the meaning of the data point values when doing statistical analysis. In the code below, we express the unique data point values that make up the sample space of the *Improvement* variable and count how many times each appears. It is important to clearly understand that the variable type is not numerical.

Express the unique data point values in the *Improvement* column and their counts:

In[11]:= **data[Counts, "Improvement"]**

Out[11]=

0	301
1	296

It is just as important to understand that although the *Improvement* variable was expressed in terms of numbers, there is no order to them. One may follow zero in our natural counting system, but these values represented ideas, i.e. improvement and no improvement. There is no order to these data point values.

For ordered categorical variables, we have the *ordinal* categorical data type. Consider the *SurveyQuestion1* variable. Let's assume the question was, "Rate how much you enjoyed the airline food," with 1 referring to *not so tasty* all the way to 5 for *gourmet meal*. Be careful. Although these are numbers and we can order them (hence ordinal categorical), they do not represent actual numbers. For one, there is no fixed difference between them. We cannot imply that the difference in taste between values 1 and 2 is the same as between 3 and 4. Neither can we say that someone who chose 4 found the food twice as tasty as someone who chose 2. Strictly speaking then, we cannot represent this data with a mean value. We may be able to calculate a mean, but how do we interpret a result such as 2.4? How tasty is airline food if it is rated as 2.4?

Now that we have a good classification system for the data type for our variables, we can choose an appropriate statistical test when we do our analysis. There is one more classification system for numerical data types that we should look at first though.

Discrete and Continuous Data Types

Numerical data types can either be *discrete* or *continuous*. Let's have a look at the *Age* variable again. The sample space comes from integers, which are discrete values. The number 46.8 is a decimal value and not an integer. We know, though, that years can be broken down into weeks, days, hours, and so on, so it makes sense to say that the mean age was 46.5 years. *Age*, in this case, is then a *continuous* numerical variable. The same goes for currency (dollars, euros, and pounds). We might have a smallest value for any given currency on earth, but for banks to keep proper track of interest rates, very small decimal values might have to be used.

When data point values can absolutely only take certain numerical values, we refer to them as being *discrete* numerical. As a very simple example, we can look at the roll of a die. For a normal six-sided die, the value that lands face up can only be an integer value from one through six.

Exercises

5.1 Calculate the number of unique data point values in the *InsulinDependentDiabetic* column in the dataset used in this chapter.

5.2 Calculate the number of unique data point values in the *SurveyQuestion1* column.

5.3 What data type would you consider the *TreatmentGroup* variable to be?

5.4 What data type would you consider the *HB* column to to be?

5.5 Calculate the minimum and maximum values in the *HB* column.

Tech Notes

- The semicolon suppresses output to the screen and is often used in larger blocks of code to eliminate unnecessary lines of output.

- When more than one argument is passed, it needs to be represented as a list.

More to Explore

For more information, try the Computation with Structured Datasets guide page (wolfr.am/StructuredDatasets)

For an advanced application, try N. M. Abbassi's Wolfram Demonstration on continuous- to discrete-time fourier transforms (wolfr.am/TimeFourierTransform)

6 | Simple Descriptive Statistics

Assuming that data collection has been completed properly, our first task in any data analysis project is to summarize the data. Human beings are simply not designed to stare at rows and rows of data point values and make any sense of them. Instead, we extract single values that are representative of the whole.

Data point values hide information. It is our duty to explore and find that information through the many steps of data analysis. Summary or descriptive statistics is that first step.

We looked at a variety of data types in the previous chapter. In this chapter, we are going to do our first statistical analysis by way of describing our data. In order to accomplish this, we will create a variety of random data point values for a set of given variables, simulating real-world experiments. We will also use a variety of data types.

The Wolfram Language provides for an easy way to generate List objects containing random data point values.

Creating List Objects

Let's start by supposing we have an experiment that involves 50 humans and that we will therefore have 50 data point values for each variable. The first variable is *age*. Age represents a continuous, numerical data type, although we mostly capture this data as integers.

In the following example, we use the RandomInteger function and ask for 50 values, taken at random from the domain 18 through 80 years. Each execution of the line of code to generate these 50 values will yield a different set of values. As mentioned, this means that when you run this code, it will produce different values.

The RandomInteger function, as the name implies, returns a random integer value. We can specify the domain from which to choose. The lowest and highest values are placed in curly braces, as they represent a List object. Following a comma, we can specify how many values we require.

In the code below, we will assign the computer variable name **age** to our list of values.

Seed the pseudorandom number generator with an arbitrary integer. Create a List with 50 data point values from a constant distribution:

```
In[1]:= SeedRandom[12]
        age = RandomInteger[{18, 80}, 50]
```

Out[2]= {27, 18, 64, 51, 55, 69, 24, 64, 46, 27, 39, 24, 46, 58, 39, 32, 48, 26, 39, 77, 29, 43, 46, 33, 27, 67, 43, 40, 75, 57, 67, 31, 33, 51, 62, 80, 19, 51, 62, 30, 47, 49, 66, 36, 40, 39, 76, 73, 36, 73}

Randomly generated values are not absolutely random; instead, they are termed pseudorandom as they are produced by an algorithm. The SeedRandom function allows for control over this random value creation. By seeding the pseudorandom number generator with an integer value, we can get reproducible results. After using the SeedRandom function, the same values will be returned. This makes the code reproducible. It means that when you run the code again, the same values will be selected. In the code below, we overwrite the **age** variable. The SeedRandom function takes an integer of your choice as the argument. Every chosen integer will reproduce a different set of values. In this text, we will use the arbitrary value 123.

Overwrite **age** to get a specified selection:

```
In[3]:= SeedRandom[123]
        age = RandomInteger[{18, 80}, 50]
```

Out[4]= {47, 28, 58, 20, 43, 75, 50, 75, 53, 76, 38, 62, 68, 56, 27, 52, 19, 33, 23, 72, 50, 78, 73, 72, 43, 28, 79, 55, 33, 23, 47, 37, 48, 67, 43, 31, 43, 60, 66, 27, 76, 41, 55, 25, 47, 76, 31, 55, 71, 34}

Our next variable, which we will call *q1*, represents the answer selected for a survey question. Each participant in our experiment read the statement and could choose one of the following answers: *totally disagree, disagree, neither agree not disagree, agree,* or *totally agree.* There are five possible items to select from. This type of selection is an example of a Likert-style question.

We can represent the selection made by each participant as a digit, 1 through 5. Even though these are numbers, they represent a categorical data type and we should not interpret this as a numerical data type. We can consider some order in the variable data point values, and as such, we view this variable as ordinal categorical. In keeping with the variable name, we will call the computer variable that holds our List object **q1**.

Create a list of 50 random integers:

```
In[5]:= SeedRandom[123]
        q1 = RandomInteger[{1, 5}, 50]
```

Out[6]= {4, 2, 3, 1, 1, 3, 4, 2, 2, 5, 1, 2, 5, 4, 3, 3, 5, 5, 3, 5, 2, 2, 5, 3, 1, 2, 2, 1, 5, 1, 5, 4, 2, 2, 3, 5, 2, 1, 4, 3, 4, 4, 2, 4, 2, 2, 4, 2, 3, 1}

The next variable is *country* (computer variable name country), and it represents the country of birth for each participant. This variable is a nominal categorical data type. Imagine that they are all from one of five countries (the sample space). We use the RandomChoice function for this variable. The function takes a List object containing strings; hence, we use curly braces and quotations marks. After the comma, we specify that we want 50 random values.

Create country with a list of 50 values, each chosen at random from a list of five countries:

In[7]:= **SeedRandom[123]**
   country =
   RandomChoice[{"USA", "Canada", "Great Britain", "France", "Germany"}, 50]

Out[8]= {France, Canada, Great Britain, USA, USA, Great Britain, France, Canada, Canada, Germany, USA, Canada, Germany, France, Great Britain, Great Britain, Germany, Germany, Great Britain, Germany, Canada, Canada, Germany, Great Britain, USA, Canada, Canada, USA, Germany, USA, Germany, France, Canada, Canada, Great Britain, Germany, Canada, USA, France, Great Britain, France, France, Canada, France, Canada, Canada, France, Canada, Great Britain, USA}

Our last variable is *height* (computer variable name height). This represents the height of each participant. It is a continuous, numerical data type. We will use the RandomInteger function again, specifying a domain of 150 to 196 (this is in centimeters) and 50 values.

Height in centimeters for 50 participants chosen from the integer sample space 150 through 196:

In[9]:= **SeedRandom[123]**
   height = RandomInteger[{150, 196}, 50]

Out[10]= {179, 160, 190, 152, 175, 182, 185, 170, 194, 188, 159, 184, 151, 165, 155, 182, 175, 160, 187, 165, 155, 179, 169, 180, 175, 163, 175, 192, 159, 173, 187, 157, 179, 163, 187, 166, 164, 153, 180, 157, 170, 185, 153, 168, 167, 184, 196, 175, 186, 188}

Our variables contain a relatively large number of values and words. When viewed as such, it is difficult to make sense of it. It becomes much easier to grasp when we summarize these data point values by replacing them with values that are representative of the whole.

You will note that research papers show summarized data values without showing the actual set of all values. Instead, summary values are used to convey the essence of the data to the reader. This summary is also the first step toward understanding what the research data is trying to tell us.

There are three common methods of representing a set of values by a single number—the mean, the median, and the mode. Collectively, these are all *measures of central tendency*, alternatively called *point estimates*.

Most papers will also describe the spread of the data points, also known as *measures of dispersion*. This is where you will come across terms such as *range*, *quartiles*, *percentiles*, *variance*, and the more common *standard deviation*, often abbreviated as SD. Let's have a look.

Measures of Central Tendency

Mean (average), median, and mode are all measures of central tendency. As the name implies, they represent values that tend to the middle of all the data point values in a set. What they achieve, in reality, is to summarize a set of data point values, replacing it with a single value that is somehow representative of all the values in the set.

In order for all of this to be meaningful, the measure of central tendency must be an accurate reflection of all the actual values. No one method can suffice for this purpose, and therefore, we look at the three common ones.

Mean

The mean, or average, refers to the simple mathematical operation of adding up all the data point values for a variable in a set and dividing that sum by the number of values in the set. It is a meaningful way to represent a set of numbers that do not have outliers (values that are very different from the large majority of numbers).

The equation for the mean of a set of numerical values is given in (1) below.

$$\mu = \frac{\sum_{i=1}^{n} x_i}{n} \tag{1}$$

The symbol μ is typically used to represent the mean of a variable in a population. The $\sum$ symbol is shorthand notation for summing or adding. Each of the values in the List object containing the numerical values is represented by $x_1, x_2, \ldots$, with the i playing the part of each of the ordered values in the List object. Finally, n is the total number of values in the List object. As mentioned, we use the Greek symbol μ when calculating the mean of a population. When we have data point values for a sample, we use the symbol $\bar{x}$. Here, the x is a placeholder for the variable name.

Let's look at how to use the Wolfram Language to easily calculate the mean values for our variables **age** and **height**. It is achieved by using the function Mean, which, simply takes our computer variable that holds the appropriate List object. Below we use postfix notation to get a numerical result.

Calculate the mean of **age**:

In[11]:= **Mean[age] // N**

Out[11]= 49.78

Calculate the mean of **height**:

In[12]:= **Mean[height] // N**

Out[12]= 172.86

There are other forms of the mean. One you might often come across is the geometric mean. Instead of adding all the values, we multiply them and then take the nth root of the multiplication, where n represents the number of elements. The geometric mean is shown by the expression (2) below.

$$\sqrt[n]{\prod |x_i|} \qquad (2)$$

Here, n is again the sample size and the $\prod$ symbol refers to the product (multiplication) of values. The Wolfram Language function is GeometricMean.

Calculate the geometric mean of height:

In[13]:= **GeometricMean[height] // N**

Out[13]= **172.399**

Median

If we had the values 1, 2, 3, 4, and 100, you could well imagine that the last value was an outlier. If we calculated a mean, it would be 22, since the values add to 110 and there are 5 of them and 5 divides 110 exactly 22 times. We could all agree that 22 is somehow not representative of the five values. The median would be more appropriate to use as a measure of central tendency in our example of the values 1, 2, 3, 4, and 100, e.g. in the case of outliers. The median chooses a value for which half of the total number of values are *less than* and the other half are *more than* it. In our example of 1, 2, 3, 4 and 100, there are five numbers. The number 3 would be the median since there are two numbers, 1 and 2 that are less than it and two numbers, 4 and 100 that are greater than it. You would agree that the number 3 is a more representative point estimate for our five numbers than the average, which was 22.

If there are an even number of values, we simply take the average of the middle two, e.g. the median of 1, 2, 3, 4 is 2.5 since the middle two values are 2 and 3 and their mean is 2.5. In the Wolfram Language, we use the Median function. Let's calculate the median for our two numerical variables.

Calculate the median of age:

In[14]:= **Median[age] // N**

Out[14]= **49.**

Calculate the median of height:

In[15]:= **Median[height] // N**

Out[15]= **175.**

Notice how close they are to the means of these two variables. The message that we can take away from this is that there probably are not many outliers (at least in one direction, i.e. either very small or very large) in the List objects for age and height. We will learn much more about this in Chapter 10, which is all about parametric tests.

Mode

The mode is the data point value that occurs most frequently in a set. As such, it is convenient to use when the variable is of categorical type. At times, there might be more than one data point value that occurs most frequently. In such cases, the set is multimodal.

In the Wolfram Language, we make use of the Counts function. It will count the number of occurrences (frequency) of each unique data point value in a List object. In the code below, we use it to count the frequency at which the five countries appear in the countries variable.

Count how many times each unique country appears in the List object:

In[16]:= **Counts[country]**

Out[16]= <| France → 9, Canada → 15, Great Britain → 9, USA → 8, Germany → 9 |>

You may be wondering what type of object the Counts function returns. We can always use the Head function to find out. Below we pass the function Counts, with its own argument of country, as the argument of the Head function.

Evaluate the code to find out what object the function Head returns:

In[17]:= **Head[Counts[country]]**

Out[17]= Association

Each unique *key* (country) is associated with a *value* (a count in this case), hence, an Association object.

Another Wolfram Language function that we can use is the Tally function. It returns a nested List object. Each subList object contains two elements. The first is the unique data point value and the second is the number of times it appears.

Tally is an alternative function to count frequencies:

In[18]:= **Tally[country]**

Out[18]= {{France, 9}, {Canada, 15}, {Great Britain, 9}, {USA, 8}, {Germany, 9}}

We can use the Sort function to sort the values in the Association created by the Counts function. It can take a second argument to sort the return in ascending or descending order. In the case below, we use Greater to indicate that we want the sorting in descending order (i.e. greatest first).

Sort the counts in descending order:

In[19]:= **Sort[Counts[country], Greater]**

Out[19]= <| Canada → 15, Germany → 9, Great Britain → 9, France → 9, USA → 8 |>

The value, or sometimes values, that occurs most commonly is the mode of the List object.

Measures of Dispersion

Whereas point estimates summarize data point values by using a single value, measures of dispersion give us an idea of how spread out the values are. Together with point estimates, they give us an excellent summary of our data. Let's have a look at some common measures.

Range

The range is simply the difference between the minimum and maximum numerical values in a set. A common variable to express as a range is age, where we may want to report the youngest and oldest patient in a set.

To get the minimum value in a List object that contains numerical data point values, we use the Min function, and for the maximum value, we use the Max function. The range is simply the difference between the two.

Find the minimum age:

In[20]:= **Min[age]**

Out[20]= 19

Find the maximum age:

In[21]:= **Max[age]**

Out[21]= 79

Calculate the range:

In[22]:= **Max[age] − Min[age]**

Out[22]= 60

Use the MinMax function to return both of these descriptive values:

In[23]:= **MinMax[age]**

Out[23]= {19, 79}

Together with the mean, we may now report the minimum and maximum values or range in a paper.

Quartiles

Whereas the median divides a set of data point values into halves, quartiles divide it into quarters. Quartiles have a zeroth value, which represents the minimum value of a set of values, and a fourth quartile, which represents the maximum value.

The first quartile represents the value in the data point set that divides the set into two parts, the first of which represents a quarter of the values, all being smaller than the first quartile value, and the second part, consisting of three quarters of the values, all being larger than that first quartile value.

The second quartile value divides the data point set into equal parts and is nothing other than the median.

As you must have inferred by now, the third quartile represents the value in the data point set that divides the set into two parts, with three quarters of the values being smaller than the third quartile value and one quarter being larger than that value.

The Quartiles function in the Wolfram Language returns the values for the first, second, and third quartiles. In the code cell below, we calculate these values for our age List object.

Calculate the values for the first, second, and third quartiles:

In[24]:= **Quartiles[age]**

Out[24]= {33, 49, 67}

Interquartile Range

The interquartile range (IQR) is the difference between the first and third quartile values. The function that accomplishes this task is InterquartileRange.

Calculate the interquartile range:

In[25]:= **InterquartileRange[age]**

Out[25]= 34

As an exercise, we can use indexing on the List object of values returned by the Quartiles function to check if the IQR returned by the Interquartile function is correct. This is accomplished by subtracting the first value from the third.

Verify that our IQR is correct:

In[26]:= **Quartiles[age][[3]] – Quartiles[age][[1]]**

Out[26]= 34

The IQR is useful when looking for outliers. If we multiply the IQR by 1.5 and add this value to the third quartile value and similarly subtract it from the first quartile value, we will have created a new maximum and minimum value, beyond which any data point values in a set can be considered statistical outliers. This is beautifully demonstrated in a box-and-whisker plot, which we will see in the next chapter.

Quantiles

Whereas quartiles simply divide a set of values into four equal parts, we can be much more precise with the division of a List object using quantiles. With quantiles, we can specify any division of the data point values.

The Quantile function in the Wolfram Language takes two arguments. The first is the List object and the second is either a single value or another List object specifying the division, in both cases, provided as decimals. In the code below, we calculate the quantiles 0.1 through 0.9. It is common to see the term *percentiles*, which simply expressed the fractions of division of the data as percentages. In this case, the code below therefore calculates the 10th to the 90th percentile.

Quantiles (or percentiles) are easy to interpret. The 0.1 quantile (10th percentile) will return the value in the List object for which 10% of the values are less than and 90% are greater than.

Calculate the quantile values 0.1 through 0.9:

In[27]:= **Quantile[age, {0.1, 0.2, 0.3, 0.4, 0.5, 0.6, 0.7, 0.8, 0.9}]**

Out[27]= {25, 31, 37, 43, 48, 55, 60, 71, 75}

Variance and Standard Deviation

The method of describing the extent of dispersion or spread of data point values in relation to the mean is referred to as the *variance*. We often use the square root of the variance, which is called the *standard deviation* (SD).

Imagine all the data point values in a set are represented by dots on a straight line, i.e. the familiar x axis from graphs at school. A dot can also be placed on this line representing the mean value. Now the *distance* between each point and the mean is taken, creating a new set of values, which is then averaged in order to get an average distance, i.e. how far all the points are from the mean. Note that we want distance away from the mean, i.e. not negative values (some values will be smaller than the mean). For this mathematical reason, all the differences are squared, resulting in all positive values, resulting in the variance.

The mathematical equation for the variance is given in (3).

$$\frac{\sum (x_i - \mu)^2}{n} \tag{3}$$

Here the x_i values again represent each of the values in the set. The mean is subtracted from each in turn and this subtraction is squared. All of these are summed and then divided by the number of values in the set.

The square root of this is then the SD, the average distance that all the data points are away from the mean, or more appropriately stated as the difference between the values and the mean.

You will note that some texts divide by one less than the number of data point values in a set as shown in equation (4). This equation is used to calculate the variance of a *sample*, whereas dividing by the number of data point values is used to calculate the variance in a whole population.

$$\frac{\sum(x_i - \bar{x})^2}{n - 1} \tag{4}$$

As an illustration, the data values of 1, 2, 3, 20, 38, 39, and 40 have a much wider spread (standard deviation) than 17, 18, 19, 20, 21, 22, and 23. Both sets have an average of 20, but the first has a much wider spread, or SD.

We use the Variance and StandardDeviation functions to calculate variance and standard deviation.

Calculate the variance of age:

In[28]:= **Variance[age] // N**

Out[28]= 332.379

Calculate the standard deviation of age:

In[29]:= **StandardDeviation[age] // N**

Out[29]= 18.2313

Note that the SD is the square root of the variance. We can use the Sqrt function to check this.

Calculate the square root of the variance of age:

In[30]:= **Sqrt[Variance[age]] // N**

Out[30]= 18.2313

We are now well equipped to summarize our data through descriptive statistics.

Exercises

6.1 Create the following List object: variable = {5, 2, 9, 9, 3, 8, 6, 5, 5, 4, 7, 9, 8, 9, 3, 3, 3, 8, 1, 6}.

6.2 Calculate the mean value of the List object.

6.3 Calculate the median value of the List object.

6.4 Calculate the mode(s) of variable. (Note that numerical variables can also have a mode.)

6.5 Calculate the standard deviation and variance of the List object.

6.6 Calculate the minimum and maximum values of variable.

6.7 Calculate the quartile values of the List object.

6.8 Calculate the interquartile range of variable.

6.9 Select only the values in variable that are greater than 4.

Tech Notes

- As Mathematica can provide results as fractions, using postfix notation // N will assure a numeric value in the output.

- Use the **Select** function. Pass as variables the List object name and set the selection by using the ⌗ placeholder. You will note that the solution follows from selections in Dataset objects. Whereas we use datasetname[Select[⌗*column name* > *value* &]] for Dataset objects, we can use Select[*list name*, *criteria*] directly on a List object, just as we did **datasetname[Mean,** *column name*] for a Dataset object and Mean[*list name*] for a List object when calculating a mean.

- Part ([[...]]) notation can be used to pick out an element or multiple elements of an expression.

More to Explore

The Documentation Center has many resources on descriptive statistics (wolfr.am/QuPgmeKO)

S.R. Colwell submitted an excellent Demonstration on the single factor analysis of variance (wolfr.am/DYeSw9bO)

7 | Visualizing Data

We have seen the importance of measures of central tendency and dispersion to help us get a better understanding of our data. Plotting goes a few steps further by giving us a visual representation of our data. This is arguably the most important step before analyzing any data. It provides for a much deeper understanding of the data from an experiment.

Data Import

In this chapter, we will make use of a spreadsheet file. For the purposes of this chapter, it is important that you save it in the same folder or directory as the notebook file. This will allow for an easy way to import the file.

Save the notebook then set the "save" directory. Note that the semicolon suppresses output to the screen:

In[1]:= **SetDirectory[NotebookDirectory[]];**

We will use the SemanticImport function and pass the file name with its extension as argument. This returns a Wolfram Language Dataset object, which we store in the computer variable data.

Import the spreadsheet file as a Dataset object and save the data as a computer variable:

In[2]:= **data = SemanticImport["Simulation.csv"];**

We can view the first five rows of data together with the column headers using another procedure called *indexing*. By using indexing, we can view the first five rows of data. This will be displayed together with the column headers, which are the experiment's variables.

View the first five rows of the Dataset:

In[3]:= **data[;; 5]**

	SpecimenID	Category1	Variable1	Variable2	Variable3	Category2
	1	A	66	13.0	37.8	C
	2	B	33	15.7	38.6	R
Out[3]=	3	A	63	19.4	38.1	X
	4	A	63	8.8	36.5	X
	5	B	85	23.2	41.5	R

As mentioned before, note that when we view a single row of data, the Wolfram Language transforms the row into two columns. The left-hand side column displays the variable names (which are the column headers in the spreadsheet file and **Dataset** object) and the right-hand side column displays the actual data values.

Variables and data values for the first subject:

In[4]:= **data[1]**

	SpecimenID	1
	Category1	A
	Category2	C
	Category3	P
	Variable1	66
Out[4]=	Variable2	13.
	Variable3	37.8
	Variable4	1.5
	Variable5	1.8
	Variable6	98

We note a variable called *SpecimenID*. It contains an identity number for the subjects in the dataset. Following this, we note a categorical variable, three numerical variables, and a final categorical variable.

As a review of the previous chapter, let's summarize the dataset using descriptive statistics. Since we used the **SemanticImport** function, our computer variable holds a **Dataset** object.

Check the type of variable:

In[5]:= **Head[data]**

Out[5]= Dataset

This means that we should use the alternative syntax to calculate our point estimates and measures of dispersion, e.g. data[Mean, "Variable1"], unless we convert each column of data into a List object.

We'll begin by looking at the means, standard deviations, and quartiles of each of the three numerical variables, *Variable1*, *Variable2*, and *Variable3*. When referencing the Dataset object using the alternative syntax, we can actually create a list of the Wolfram Language functions that are required. In the code cell below, we calculate the values for the mean, standard deviation, and quartiles of *Variable1*.

It's easy to get the descriptive statistics Mean, StandardDeviation, and Quartiles:

In[6]:= **data[{Mean, StandardDeviation, Quartiles}, "Variable1"]**

Out[6]= 56.73	19.829	77/2	60	73

We note a mean of 56.73, a standard deviation of 19.829, a first quartile of $\frac{77}{2}$, a median (second quartile) of 60, and a third quartile of 73. Let's take a look at these statistics for *Variable2* and *Variable3*.

Use the same procedure for the other variables:

In[7]:= **data[{Mean, StandardDeviation, Quartiles}, "Variable2"]**

12.766	5.11048	9.05
Out[7]=		13.4
		15.8

In[8]:= **data[{Mean, StandardDeviation, Quartiles}, "Variable3"]**

37.989	2.57191	36.15
Out[8]=		38.0
		39.75

We can have a look at the mode of the two categorical variables too. In the code cells below, we use the Counts function.

Counts tells the number of unique data point values in the "Category1" variable:

In[9]:= **data[Counts, "Category1"]**

A	50
Out[9]= B	50

We note from the result that the *Category1* variable is bimodal, with both the unique data point values (sample space elements for the variable), *A* and *B*, appearing 50 times. *Category2* has a sample space of three elements.

Let's try it with the "Category2" variable:

In[10]:= **data[Counts, "Category2"]**

C	34
R	33
X	33

Out[10]=

The mode for *Category2* is *C*, as it appears most frequently.

Counts of the unique data point values for the "Category3" variable:

In[11]:= **data[Counts, "Category3"]**

P	28
Q	16
R	16
S	34
T	6

Out[11]=

We note a sample space of five data point values for *Category3*, with the "S" data value appearing as the mode.

As another reminder of how to generate a Wolfram Language List object from a column in a Dataset object, have a look at the code cell below. Remember that the Normal function returns a nested List object (List object with a single subList) and that we want to extract that subList, hence, the use of indexing. We will store this new List object in the computer variable variable1.

Remember that a nested List is returned in order to reference this subList:

In[12]:= **variable1 = Normal[data[List, "Variable1"]][[1]]**

Out[12]= {66, 33, 63, 63, 85, 33, 70, 57, 51, 52, 69, 82, 72, 57, 21, 63, 21, 88, 62, 37, 38, 39, 60, 49, 65, 39, 89, 31, 53, 34, 47, 28, 73, 31, 85, 87, 46, 84, 73, 71, 81, 74, 63, 78, 61, 21, 60, 89, 42, 35, 44, 78, 57, 39, 28, 68, 36, 64, 88, 69, 64, 73, 78, 28, 50, 71, 74, 75, 83, 54, 46, 82, 66, 65, 49, 76, 53, 70, 25, 37, 81, 38, 70, 35, 30, 37, 27, 21, 43, 66, 85, 23, 51, 34, 69, 44, 75, 45, 87, 51}

Because variable1 is a List object, we can now use functions such as Mean in its standard form:

In[13]:= **Mean[variable1] // N**

Out[13]= 56.73

Now that we have a good idea of what the data is trying to tell us through the use of summary statistics, let's have a look at the basic plots in the Wolfram Language.

The List Plot

The ListPlot function plots a list of values on a Cartesian plane in the form of points, each with an x coordinate and a y coordinate. If we only have a single List, the index (position) of each value is taken sequentially and forms the x coordinate of each of the values. The actual values in the List form the corresponding y coordinates.

We start by creating a List using the Table function. We will assign this to a computer variable called yValues.

Create a list of 10 values starting at 1 and ending at 10 with a step size of 1:

In[14]:= **yValues = Table[i, {i, 1, 10, 1}]**

Out[14]= {1, 2, 3, 4, 5, 6, 7, 8, 9, 10}

The Range function with an appropriate argument will create the same List.

You can use Range with an argument value of 10:

In[15]:= **Range[10]**

Out[15]= {1, 2, 3, 4, 5, 6, 7, 8, 9, 10}

Now for the ListPlot function. We pass the yValues object as an argument. As mentioned, the ListPlot function will create x axis coordinates in order, starting at 1 with increments of 1, corresponding to the position of each element in the list.

ListPlot[Range[10]] will create the same plot:

In[16]:= **ListPlot[yValues]**

Out[16]=

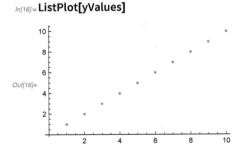

Or use both functions nested:

In[17]:= **ListPlot[Range[10]]**

Out[17]=

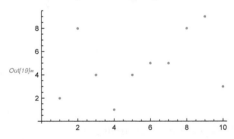

The result is a very neat plot with multiple points. They have coordinates (1, 1), (2, 2), and so on. Irrespective of the values in a List, they will always be plotted against a sequential element index value on the *x* axis starting at 1. Let's see this in action by creating 10 random integers stored in the computer variable randomValues and plotting them.

The RandomInteger function requires the interval to be a List and the total number of values required:

In[18]:= **randomValues = RandomInteger[{1, 10}, 10]**

Out[18]= {2, 8, 4, 1, 4, 5, 5, 8, 9, 3}

In[19]:= **ListPlot[randomValues]**

Out[19]=

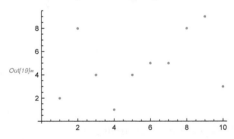

The Wolfram Language comes equipped with a number of styles:

In[20]:= **ListPlot[randomValues, PlotTheme → "Marketing"]**

Out[20]=

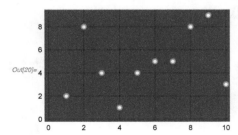

Once you have executed a cell, you will notice the *suggestion bar* that opens up below it. In the previous plot, we see a darker background. Wolfram Language code was automatically generated to create this option. It was applied by simply clicking on the **Theme** link on the suggestion bar and selecting **Marketing**. The code is interesting because it shows us a new argument that we can pass to the ListPlot function. There are many such arguments and they allow us to change various aspects of a plot.

In[20]:= **ListPlot[randomValues, PlotTheme → "Marketing"]**

The Scatter Plot

It would be much more common to plot two numerical variables against each other on a scatter plot. The value for one variable can be the x coordinate of a point and the value from another variable can be the y coordinate. Typically, for each dot (marker) in a scatter plot, we are considering the values for two variables for a single subject in a set of data. What we are visualizing here is a correlation between two numerical variables.

To start, we will create a nested List. Each subList will be a pair of values for our two coordinates. Imagine that there are 10 measurements for each of two variables for eight participants in an experiment. In the code cell below, we create such a nested List and store it in the computer variable pairedValues.

Let's create 10 sublists, each with two elements from the domain of values 1 through 10:

In[21]:= **pairedvalues = RandomInteger[{1, 10}, {10, 2}]**

Out[21]= {{4, 4}, {5, 5}, {6, 4}, {3, 1}, {4, 6}, {2, 6}, {10, 4}, {3, 4}, {5, 3}, {3, 5}}

Each subList contains a pair of values that can be used as the coordinates of a dot on a scatter plot.

We can use the TableForm function in the Wolfram Language to visualize this:

In[22]:= **TableForm[pairedValues]**

Out[22]//TableForm=

9	9
1	3
4	10
1	5
5	5
8	7
8	7
8	1
2	8
7	10

Plot these as coordinate points on a scatter plot using the ListPlot function:

In[23]:= **ListPlot[pairedValues]**

Out[23]=
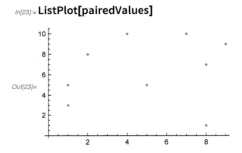

Now, let's get to our imported Dataset and use *Variable1* and *Variable2* as our coordinates.

Since we are dealing with a Dataset object, we make use of the alternative syntax to create a plot, much as we did when calculating our summary statistics. Note that we specify the column headers (variable names) in quotation marks.

Note the placement of the variable names inside of quotation marks:

In[24]:= **data[ListPlot, {"Variable1", "Variable2"}]**

Out[24]=
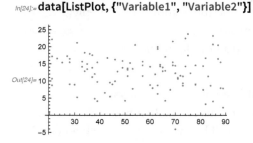

To get some practice with the Wolfram Language, let's create a List of paired values that are correlated. We can use the Table function for this. We will make the y coordinate variable twice the value of the x coordinate value and add a random value to each. This nested List is stored in the computer variable pairs.

The first segment is just a list of 1 to 20. The second segment takes the first and multiplies it by 2, then adds a random value between −2 and 2:

In[25]:= **pairs = Table[{i, 2 ∗ i + RandomReal[{−2, 2}]}, {i, 1, 20, 1}]**

Out[25]= {{1, 1.43711}, {2, 5.95417}, {3, 6.59684}, {4, 7.70232}, {5, 10.8817},
{6, 11.4347}, {7, 12.6587}, {8, 14.4268}, {9, 16.2926}, {10, 21.0331},
{11, 20.2389}, {12, 22.567}, {13, 27.5771}, {14, 27.0274}, {15, 29.5622},
{16, 30.2318}, {17, 32.8204}, {18, 34.9886}, {19, 37.1333}, {20, 38.3932}}

Let's plot it and see what it looks like:

In[26]:= **ListPlot[pairs]**

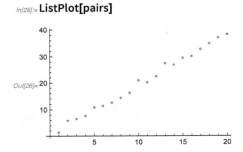

As by our design, note that as the variable on the x axis increases in value, so does the variable on the y axis.

The Bubble Chart

A bubble chart allows us to add a third variable to a scatter plot by using the data point values for that variables to represent the size of each dot. We will add a third variable to a nested List similar to the one that we created above using the Table function. The third variable will be a random integer on the interval 25 to 75, indicating the size of the bubble. In the code cell below, the nested List object is stored as threeVariables.

We simply add a third element to each nested List:

In[27]:= **threeVariables =**
Table[{i, 2 ∗ i + RandomReal[{−2, 2}], RandomInteger[{25, 75}]}, {i, 1, 20, 1}]

Out[27]= {{1, 1.89556, 26}, {2, 2.75499, 26}, {3, 7.93171, 69}, {4, 9.97807, 30}, {5, 10.2815, 56},
{6, 10.0747, 53}, {7, 14.5294, 47}, {8, 15.0573, 28}, {9, 16.6738, 54}, {10, 18.6435, 63},
{11, 22.6681, 75}, {12, 25.0632, 33}, {13, 26.9459, 35}, {14, 28.0586, 40}, {15, 28.2632, 27},
{16, 30.9638, 54}, {17, 35.0165, 47}, {18, 34.8571, 53}, {19, 36.0393, 32}, {20, 39.2989, 51}}

Let's plot this third dimension.

Plot threeVariables using a scatter plot, where the first two elements of each subList make up the *x* and *y* coordinates and the third element defines the size of each dot:

In[28]:= **BubbleChart[threeVariables]**

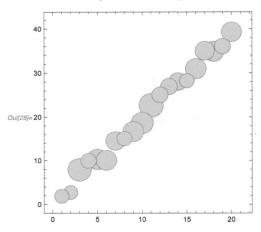

We have introduced more visual information to represent our third variable by the size of each dot.

The Box-and-Whisker Chart

One of the most commonly used plots in statistics and data analysis is the box-and-whisker chart, which represents the values for a numerical variable on the *y* axis. Let's consider the visual parts of this type of plot.

The central box in a box-and-whisker plot has as its upper edge the value of the third quartile for that variable. The bottom edge represents the value of the first quartile. The line in the box represents the median, or second quartile value.

Above and below the central box are two whiskers. Their outer limits represent the maximum and minimum values for the specific variable. If outliers are identified, the outer limits will be 1.5 times the interquartile range above and below the third and first quartiles, respectively. These outliers appear as dots beyond the whiskers.

Let's create a list of random data point values for a variable and create a box-and-whisker chart for it.

Create 100 data point values in the domain 10 through 100 and store them as the variable boxVariable:

In[29]:= **boxVariable = RandomInteger[{10, 100}, 100];**

The Wolfram Language function used to create a box-and-whisker chart is called BoxWhiskerChart.

To add the outliers (if any exist), we add the "Outliers" argument:

In[30]:= **BoxWhiskerChart[boxVariable, "Outliers"]**

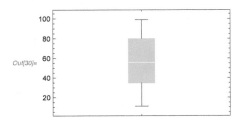

Hovering with your cursor over the box element will show summary statistics in the form of the minimum and maximum values, as well as the three quartile values.

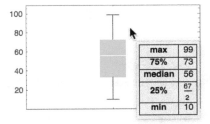

The box-and-whisker chart allows us to add more than one category for the variable. Let's consider then the ages of three groups of subjects. A separate chart element will be created for each of the List objects that we create below.

Let's create three lists of 50 people, each of varying ages:

In[31]:= **ageGroup1 = RandomInteger[{20, 80}, 50];**
ageGroup2 = RandomInteger[{30, 70}, 50];
ageGroup3 = RandomInteger[{15, 90}, 50];

The "Outliers" argument will plot any suspected outliers:

In[34]:= **BoxWhiskerChart[{ageGroup1, ageGroup2, ageGroup3}, "Outliers"]**

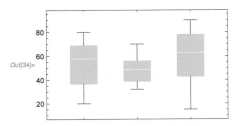

From the previous chart, we have no idea what the three chart elements refer to. Below, we add a title and chart labels to make this clear. The PlotLabel argument allows us to add a title and the ChartLabels option allows for a List of string elements to correspond to our three List objects. The arrows are created by simply typing a minus (–) followed by a greater than (>) sign.

Keep track of the order in which the lists are passed so that the order can be reflected in the ChartLabels list:

In[35]:= **BoxWhiskerChart[{ageGroup1, ageGroup2, ageGroup3}, "Outliers",**
   PlotLabel → "Group Ages", ChartLabels → {"Group 1", "Group 2", "Group 3"}]

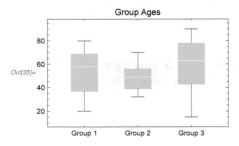

By adding a chart style using the ChartStyle option, we can use legends instead of labels. Because the three chart elements were entered as three List objects, all of the colors will be similar. The Wolfram Language contains many theme colors, and chart styling will bring different colors to each element. In the chart below, we actually specify the different colors.

Note that the style elements outside of the data are separated by commas, remaining within the closing bracket for the chart:

In[36]:= **BoxWhiskerChart[{ageGroup1, ageGroup2, ageGroup3},**
   "Outliers", PlotLabel → "Group Ages", ChartLegends → {"1", "2", "3"},
   ChartStyle → {LightGray, Gray, Black}]

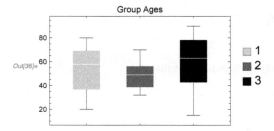

As before, we can hover over the chart elements to bring tooltips to the screen that display the summary statistics. This might include fractions. To display numerical values, we can use the // N postfix notation.

Another element that might add value is the mean, which we can display as a diamond-shaped marker.

"Diamond" and "Notched" are established specifications for BoxWhiskerChart:

In[37]:= **BoxWhiskerChart[{ageGroup1, ageGroup2, ageGroup3}, "Diamond",
    PlotLabel → "Group Ages", ChartLabels → {"Group 1", "Group 2", "Group 3"}] // N**

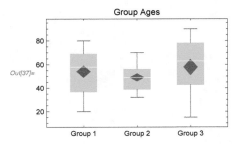

The Histogram

The histogram is a frequency chart that counts the occurrences of data point values for a numerical variable. If the numerical variable is of the continuous type, this might be more difficult, as there are many possible unique values. To solve this, we create bins. In the example below, we use the **ageGroup1** variable that we created previously.

Simply by using the Histogram function and passing the variable as an argument, we create a histogram with a default bin size:

In[38]:= **Histogram[ageGroup1]**

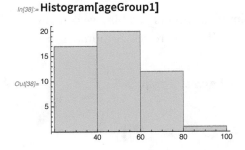

The Wolfram Language chose a bin size of 20. Therefore, you will have noted rectangular boxes of size 20 at its base. The histogram gives us the total number of ages between 20 and 40, between 40 and 60, and so on.

The Histogram function allows us to specify the bin size.

We can specify the bin size by adding an argument enclosed in curly braces:

In[39]:= **Histogram[ageGroup1, {10}]**

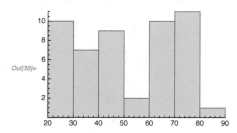

Out[39]=

We can also use data from a Dataset object.

We can plot a single variable histogram from a Dataset object. Below is a histogram of the "Variable1" data point values for the data:

In[40]:= **data[Histogram, "Variable1"]**

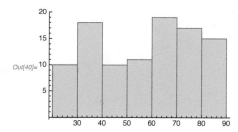

Out[40]=

Instead of counting how many times a data point value occurs in a bin, we can also express the relative frequency with which it occurs. This expresses the number of values in the bin as a fraction of the whole.

This frequency distribution form of the histogram can be created by passing the "Probability" argument:

In[41]:= **Histogram[ageGroup1, {10}, "Probability"]**

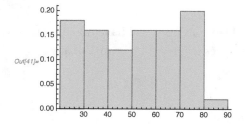

Out[41]=

To create a histogram with more than one variable selected from a Dataset will require us to extract the values as List objects first.

When we hover over each bin in a histogram, we get a tooltip that shows the count or frequency.

Use the LabelingFunction option so that these values will be added automatically:

In[42]:= **Histogram[ageGroup1, {10}, LabelingFunction → Above]**

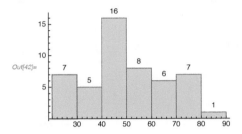

Histograms need not be vertical. They can start from any of the four sides.

The BarOrigin option allows us to specify bottom (default), left, right, or top:

In[43]:= **Histogram[ageGroup1, {10}, BarOrigin → Left]**

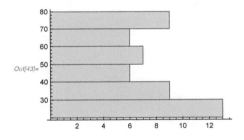

In[44]:= **Histogram[ageGroup1, {10}, BarOrigin → Top]**

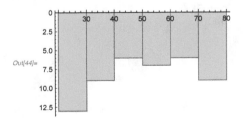

The Smooth Histogram

Instead of showing rectangles with a bin size, we can visualize a curve of the data using the SmoothHistogram function.

It works similarly to the Histogram function:

In[45]:= **SmoothHistogram[ageGroup1]**

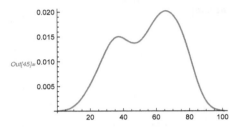

We can pass a nested list so as to generate more than one smooth histogram element.

Plot all three of our age groups and add a title to our chart using the PlotLabel option:

In[46]:= **SmoothHistogram[{ageGroup1, ageGroup2, ageGroup3},**
PlotLabel → "Age Distribution of the Three Groups"]

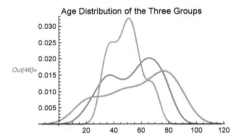

A variety of filling options are available for visual appeal. Let's fill to the *x* axis:

In[47]:= **SmoothHistogram[{ageGroup1, ageGroup2, ageGroup3},**
Filling → Axis, PlotLabel → "Age Distribution of the Three Groups"]

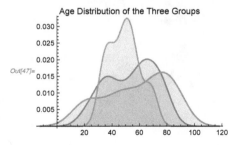

Smooth histograms can give us an early indication that we may have a statistically significant difference between two or more groups. Below we create two List objects representing a variable for two groups named group1Length and group2Length. Note the use of the RandomVariate function and the NormalDistribution function as these will be covered in the next chapter.

Plot two sets of one hundred values taken at random from a normal distribution with means of 100 and 80 and both with a standard deviation of 5:

In[48]:= **group1Length = RandomVariate[NormalDistribution[100, 5], 100];**
group2Length = RandomVariate[NormalDistribution[80, 5], 100];
SmoothHistogram[{group1Length, group2Length}]

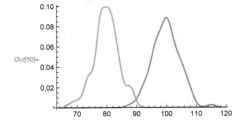

Out[50]=

The Pie Chart

The Wolfram Language makes provisions for the pie chart to accomplish the same objectives as the bar chart. The total number of unique data point values is expressed as a whole. The size of each wedge represents the relative count that each unique value takes up. Chart labels can be added and the naming should follow the same order as that expressed by the Counts function. Hovering gives us the count values.

Create a pie chart with chart labels. Be careful in which order the chart labels are entered:

In[51]:= **PieChart[Counts[category3], ChartLabels → {"P", "Q", "R", "S", "T"}]**

Out[51]=

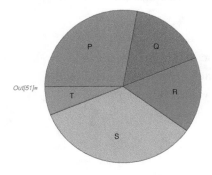

Conclusion

There is so much more that you can do with plots and I urge you to explore the Documentation Center.

The value of plots cannot be overemphasized. Plotting data adds a lot more to the story that the data wants to tell us. It is good practice to summarize and plot data before doing any data analysis.

Plots can be fun too. Below is an example taken from the Documentation Center. Enter the name of your own country to take a look at the distribution of colors that make up the flag. The code uses the CountryData function, which will download data directly from the Wolfram Research data servers.

Create a computer variable called flag to download the flag image for the United States:

In[52]:= **flag = CountryData["UnitedStates", "FlagImage"]**

Out[52]=

A list of dominant colors can be extracted using the DominantColors function. Below we pass three arguments to this function. The first is our variable name. The second is the number of colors we wish to look at. The third is a list of values we are interested in. These are the color and count. This function will return these two values and we need to create two variable names to hold them.

Create two variable names that are contained as a list and therefore require curly braces. The returned data needs to be transposed and the postfix notation is used:

In[53]:= **{color, data} = DominantColors[flag, 3, {"Color", "Count"}] // Transpose**

Out[53]= {{■, □, ■}, {4620, 3992, 2003}}

Finally, we can express this as a pie chart. Each of the data values needs to be expressed as a fraction of the total. The fraction of each color is calculated by the division of the data variable by the total of the three values. The chart style is instructed to use the color variable.

The chart labels are coded manually and must follow the same order as the color variable:

In[54]:= **PieChart[N[data / Total[data]], ChartStyle → color,**
        ChartLabels → {"Red", "White", "Blue"}]

Out[54]=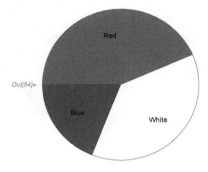

Go ahead and try your own flag.

There are many more plot types that you can learn about using the Documentation Center. We will come across some of these in the rest of the text.

Exercises

7.1   Create a scatter plot, comparing *Variable4* and *Variable5* from the imported dataset.

7.2   Extract the data point values of the *Variable6* column as a List object and save it in the computer variable named variable6.

7.3   Create a box-and-whisker plot of the variable6 object, adding a diamond to indicate the mean.

7.4   Create a histogram of variable6 from the imported dataset, with a bin size of 10.

7.5   Extract two List objects, one each for *Variable4* and *Variable5* and name them variable4 and variable5. Then use these List objects to create a smooth histogram showing the distribution of these two variables by filling the area underneath each.

7.6   Create a bar chart of the *Category1* data point values after extracting a List object named category1.

7.7   Create of pie chart of the category1 List object.

More to Explore

There are some fun descriptive statistics examples to explore on Wolfram|Alpha (wolfr.am/s40NTl8r)

For some more complicated uses of histograms, read P.-J. Letourneau's post on the Wolfram Blog (wolfr.am/s40Vlj6n)

8 | Distributions

In Chapter 6, we saw how easy it is to generate simulated data with the Wolfram Language using functions such as RandomInteger and RandomChoice. In this chapter, we will expand on this creation of data point values for variables, but in doing so, we will investigate the patterns of frequency that such values can take. These patterns are called *distributions*. The most common is the normal distribution, with its bell-shaped frequency curve.

It is important to distinguish early on between the patterns that the frequency of actual data point values take and the pattern that statistics take. In this sense, we are using the term *statistic* as some value that we calculate from data. These include values such as the mean, median, and standard deviation. Given the calculation of many mean values, we will note that they also form a frequency pattern, called a *sampling distribution*.

In the case of actual data point values for numerical variables, we find discrete and continuous distributions in line with discrete and continuous numerical data types.

In this chapter, we will learn about the most common examples of discrete, continuous, and sampling distributions.

Discrete Uniform Distribution

When we used the RandomInteger function, we were actually drawing random values from a domain, where every value in the sample space had an equal likelihood of being selected.

As an example, think for a moment about rolling a six-sided die. Each of the six sides has an equal likelihood of landing face up. If we roll the die multiple times, we can count how many times each value ends face up, that is, the frequency with which each value appears.

We can simulate this using the Wolfram Language by using the RandomInteger function to simulate 10 000 rolls of a die and store the results in the computer variable die, using a semicolon to suppress the output.

Use the SeedRandom function for reproducibility:

```
In[1]:= SeedRandom[123]
        die = RandomInteger[{1, 6}, 10 000];
```

It is important to note that a variable will retain the information assigned to it until it is overwritten or cleared using the Clear function. Keep in mind that either option will affect the results of all computations that use the variable if they are rerun. This is a useful function, especially if you are running more than one notebook at a time and are using similar computer variable names.

Clear the contents of the die computer variable:

```
In[3]:= Clear[die]
```

The RandomVariate function takes a particular distribution with its parameters as the first argument and the number of random data point values required as second argument. The distribution that we are interested in is the discrete uniform distribution. Its parameters are the minimum and maximum values. (Note that the RandomInteger and RandomChoice functions use the discrete uniform distribution. If you consult the Documentation Center, you will note that the values can also be weighted.)

Simulate a new experiment rolling a fair die 10 000 times:

```
In[4]:= SeedRandom[123]
        die = RandomVariate[DiscreteUniformDistribution[{1, 6}], 10 000];
```

We can use use the Tally function to count the occurrences of each value. It returns a nested List object of names (in this case, the values 1 through 6) and the frequency count of each of these. To return the frequencies in the order one through six, we can use the SortBy function. Its first argument is the nested List object we are creating, and the second argument is the element in the nested List object that we are interested in sorting. Since the nested List that the Tally function returns has the die face value first and then the count, we will use the First function. We will store the results in the dieCounts computer variable.

The first element in the nested list is the value being counted and the second is the actual count:

```
In[6]:= dieCounts = SortBy[Tally[die], First]
```

```
Out[6]= {{1, 1622}, {2, 1682}, {3, 1661}, {4, 1653}, {5, 1642}, {6, 1740}}
```

The Counts function can also be used. We learned that it returns an Association object, associating each name with a count:

In[7]:= **Counts[die]**

Out[7]= <| 4 → 1653, 6 → 1740, 2 → 1682, 3 → 1661, 1 → 1622, 5 → 1642 |>

Using indexing, we can collate all the second elements in each nested List object element in the dieCounts computer variable.

Store the results in the counts computer variable:

In[8]:= **counts = dieCounts⟦All, 2⟧**

Out[8]= {1622, 1682, 1661, 1653, 1642, 1740}

We can do the same with the die face values.

Store the die face values in the computer variable faceValue:

In[9]:= **faceValue = dieCounts⟦All, 1⟧**

Out[9]= {1, 2, 3, 4, 5, 6}

We can create a bar chart showing how many times each of these six values ended face up. A bar chart shows the number of specific values of a discrete or categorical variable.

Create a bar chart to show the frequency count:

In[10]:= **BarChart[counts, ChartLabels → faceValue]**

Out[10]=
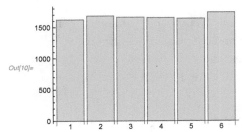

Notice the pattern that this chart shows us. All six values are (nearly) equally likely. When we count the occurrences of an event and plot it in this way, we refer to it as a *frequency distribution*.

We can use this very simple example to start to develop our intuition about probabilities and *p*-values. We develop this intuition around the concept of area, as in the area of a rectangle or the area under a curve.

From the frequency distribution, we can develop a relative frequency distribution. This is done by dividing each of the counts by the total number of cases, 10 000, in this example. We are now expressing each outcome as a fraction of the whole, which must sum to 1.

The "Probability" argument in the Histogram function allows us to visualize this relative frequency distribution. The Wolfram Language will assume a total of six bins. Look at the value on the y axis. If you run this in your own notebook, you can hover over each rectangle.

Create a histogram of probabilities. Automatic will order the x axis values:

In[11]:= **Histogram[die, Automatic, "Probability"]**

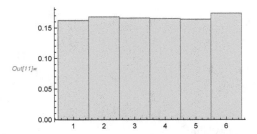

We now have a probability of rolling each of the six discrete values. Hovering over the bar representing 6, we see the probability, or p-value, of 0.174.

One way of understanding probability (and later p-values) is to consider area. In the case of the previous visualizations, the area of a rectangle. Since we are dealing with a discrete variable (which cannot be divided), we consider the width of the base of the rectangles as equal to 1. The height is given by the relative frequency. Since the area for a rectangle is base times height, we have used the area of each rectangle as the probability of our random variable taking on a specific value.

What we are trying to represent here, though, is called a probability mass function, a function that gives the probability that a discrete random variable is equal to a stated value. The term mass is used for discrete variables. Later in this chapter, we will introduce the probability density function (PDF) for continuous variables. The Wolfram Language PDF function is used in both cases.

With every discrete value having an equal probability of being selected at random, our probability mass function is an example of a discrete uniform distribution (which is why we used DiscreteUniformDistribution to create the random variable in the first place). If you roll a fair die and it lands with a 5 facing up, you could state that the probability of having rolled a 5 is $\frac{1}{6}$, the same as for any of the other values.

Use the PDF function to look at the probability mass function of the discrete uniform distribution with a sample space of values a through b. The DiscreteUniformDistribution function takes a List object as argument, representing the minimum and maximum value that the random variable can take. The second argument for the PDF function is k, representing the actual value that the variable takes.

Show the discrete uniform distribution's PDF:

In[12]:= **PDF[DiscreteUniformDistribution[{a, b}], k]**

Out[12]= $\begin{cases} \frac{1}{1-a+b} & a \le k \le b \\ 0 & \text{True} \end{cases}$

This formula states that given any number k in the closed interval a, b, the likelihood of k being selected at random can be found using the expression below.

$$\frac{1}{1 - a + b}$$

Let's look at the probability of rolling a 5 then:

In[13]:= $\dfrac{1}{1-1+6}$

Out[13]= $\dfrac{1}{6}$

Use the PDF function to show the probability of our random variable taking on a value of 5:

In[14]:= **PDF[DiscreteUniformDistribution[{1, 6}], 5]**

Out[14]= $\dfrac{1}{6}$

For our die experiment, we could use the DiscretePlot function to show the probability of each of the six values.

DiscretePlot is used to show data that has no connective data between points:

In[15]:= **DiscretePlot[PDF[DiscreteUniformDistribution[{1, 6}], x], {x, 1, 6}, PlotRange → {0, 0.2}]**

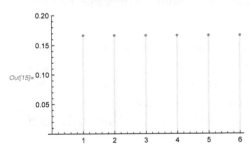

Out[15]=

Hence, values outside of these bounds (the True in the PDF above) have a zero probability of occurring. For example, we cannot roll a 7 or a 1.5.

Show that the PDF for the uniform discrete distribution of 7 is 0:

In[16]:= **PDF[DiscreteUniformDistribution[{1, 6}], 7]**

Out[16]= 0

We can also use the Probability function. It looks more like what we are trying to achieve in this equation.

$$P(x = 3 \mid \text{Discrete uniform distribution for } x \text{ being 1 through 6}) = \frac{1}{6}$$

It states that the probability of our random value taking on a value of 3 given a discrete uniform distribution with minimum value of 1 and maximum value of 6 is $\frac{1}{6}$.

Use the Probability function (note the use of (esc) dist (esc) to create the $\approx$ symbol):

In[17]:= **Probability[x == 3, x $\approx$ DiscreteUniformDistribution[{1, 6}]]**

Out[17]= $\dfrac{1}{6}$

This brings us to a very important point. The sum of all the probabilities must equal 1. This represents 100%. Given a collectively exhaustive, mutually exclusive list of outcomes, the probability of any such outcome occurring is in the interval $[0, \ 1]$, and they must all sum to 1. We cannot have a 101% probability of an outcome or a -3% probability of an outcome.

That is it for the uniform discrete distribution. Next up, we look at the normal distribution.

Normal Distribution

Most of us are familiar with the normal distribution. When plotted, the PDF for the normal distribution has a bell shape. It is also known by other names, such as the Gaussian distribution or the Laplace–Gauss distribution.

The normal distribution is useful in statistical analysis because of the central limit theorem, for which we will develop some intuition here.

We return to our die experiment, but this time, we roll a pair of dice and add the values that land face up. From experience, you might know that you are unlikely to roll two sixes, resulting in a sum of 12. You are just as unlikely to roll two ones, that is, a total of 2. It is much more likely to roll a total of 7 since we can make up 7 in so many ways. There are six ways, in fact: 1 and 6; 2 and 5; 3 and 4; 4 and 3; 5 and 2; and 6 and 1 for each respective die.

Let's create a computer variable called dice that simulates rolling a pair of dice 10 000 times and then look at the first 10 rolls using indexing.

Roll two dice 10 000 times:

In[18]:= **SeedRandom[123]**
dice = RandomVariate[DiscreteUniformDistribution[{1, 6}], {10 000, 2}];

The first 10 rolls:

In[20]:= **dice⟦ ;; 10⟧**

Out[20]= {{4, 6}, {2, 3}, {6, 1}, {1, 3}, {4, 2}, {2, 5}, {1, 2}, {5, 4}, {3, 3}, {5, 6}}

We can add all of the elements of the nested List object (pairs of rolls) using the notation below and assign it to the computer variable **totals**. We use the @@@ symbol notation. It conveniently adds up the elements in nested List objects when used in combination with the Plus function.

@@@ is shorthand notation for adding values in a nested List object:

In[21]:= **totals = Plus @@@ dice;**

If we print out the first 10 totals, we note that they are indeed the sum of each of the rolls above.

The first 10 totals:

In[22]:= **totals⟦ ;; 10⟧**

Out[22]= {10, 5, 7, 4, 6, 7, 3, 9, 6, 11}

We can add up the occurrences of each addition using the Tally function. We can also sort them from 2 through 12 using the SortBy function.

Count and sort the totals:

In[23]:= **SortBy[Tally[totals], First]**

Out[23]= {{2, 243}, {3, 547}, {4, 825}, {5, 1119}, {6, 1362},
　　　　 {7, 1710}, {8, 1394}, {9, 1086}, {10, 841}, {11, 594}, {12, 279}}

Each nested List object contains two elements. The first is the sum of the two dice and the second is how many times that value appeared in our 10 000 rolls.

Below we create a list of all the occurrences using indexing from the Tally function.

Clear the counts variable that we used previously:

In[24]:= **Clear[counts]**

Save just the counts in a computer variable called counts:

In[25]:= **counts = SortBy[Tally[totals], First]⟦All, 2⟧**

Out[25]= {243, 547, 825, 1119, 1362, 1710, 1394, 1086, 841, 594, 279}

Here is the unsurprising frequency chart, a nice symmetrically shaped curve.

Make a bar chart with manually created labels:

In[26]:= **BarChart[counts, ChartLabels → {2, 3, 4, 5, 6, 7, 8, 9, 10, 11, 12}]**

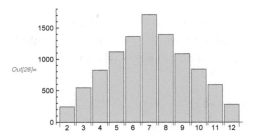

Out[26]=

Next we create a histogram and use the "Probability" option. It counts the occurrences of each of the added values, 1 through 12, and divides by 10 000 as we mentioned previously. If you run this in your own notebook, you can hover over each rectangle. It will give you the probability of rolling that value.

Create a Histogram of the probability of each value:

In[27]:= **Histogram[totals, Automatic, "Probability"]**

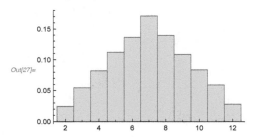

Out[27]=

Note that it also makes sense to ask what the probability is of rolling a 10 or greater (or similar question). In this case, we simply add the probabilities for the values 10, 11, and 12.

In real-life experiments, we would not be rolling dice and our numerical data types will usually be continuous. Let's imagine a variable whose data point values in the population follow a normal distribution.

If we calculate a mean of a variable for a whole population, we call that mean a *parameter* of the population. If we now take a sample of a few individuals from that population and measure the mean of the same variable (for our sample only), we call that mean a *statistic*.

The latter scenario is of course the norm. It is hardly ever possible to get detailed information from a whole population. Instead, we take a random sample from a population. Let's take a closer look at a variable for which the set of data point values for the whole population is known and, in fact, normally distributed. We will assume that this variable has the following parameters: a mean of 100 and a standard deviation of 20. The first thing we will do is plot the PDF.

The 100 and the 20 indicate a mean of 100 and a standard deviation of 20:

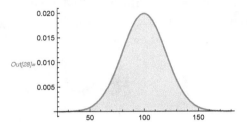

Note that it is a probability density curve. We should be able to calculate the area under the curve to calculate a probability. The obvious problem is, how? We are dealing with a continuous, numerical data type. If we were to create thin rectangles, they will have a base that, by definition, can be divided into two and so on to infinity. The number of values that a continuous numerical variable can take is, therefore, theoretically infinite. In our die rolling experiment, we divided each of the six values that our variable could take by 6. Now, though, we have to divide by infinity. Dividing by in infinity results in a 0. This gives us a 0 probability for any given value that a random continuous variable can take.

So, the probability of a random variable taking on a single value is 0. Instead, it makes more sense to ask about the probability that a variable takes on a value in an interval. More commonly, we will ask what the probability of selecting a value larger than or smaller than a specified value is. We will do just that in Chapter 10.

Note that the NormalDistribution function in the Wolfram Language takes two arguments: the first is the mean and the second is the standard deviation. These two parameters are sufficient to specify the normal probability density function. We can use the Mean, StandardDeviation, and Variance functions to examine this. In the next example, we use the symbol μ to indicate mean and σ to indicate standard deviation. In general though, remember that we use μ for the population mean and $\bar{x}$ for a sample mean.

Calculate the mean of a normal distribution with a mean of μ:

In[29]:= **Mean[NormalDistribution[μ, σ]]**

Out[29]= μ

Calculate the standard deviation of a normal distribution with a standard deviation of σ:

In[30]:= **StandardDeviation[NormalDistribution[μ, σ]]**

Out[30]= σ

Note that the variance is the standard deviation squared:

In[31]:= **Variance[NormalDistribution[μ, σ]]**

Out[31]= σ^2

The *standard normal distribution* is a special version of the normal distribution where the mean is 0 and the standard deviation is 1. When we omit the arguments for the NormalDistribution function, the Wolfram Language assumes these values.

Find the mean of the standard normal distribution:

In[32]:= **Mean[NormalDistribution[]]**

Out[32]= 0

Find the standard deviation of the standard normal distribution:

In[33]:= **StandardDeviation[NormalDistribution[]]**

Out[33]= 1

The expression for the PDF of the normal distribution is shown below.

$$\frac{1}{\sqrt{2\,\pi\sigma^2}}\,e^{\frac{-(x-\mu)^2}{2\sigma^2}}$$

We can use the Wolfram Language function PDF to show this equation:

In[34]:= **PDF[NormalDistribution[μ, σ], x]**

Out[34]= $\dfrac{e^{-\frac{(x-\mu)^2}{2\sigma^2}}}{\sqrt{2\pi}\,\sigma}$

For the standard normal distribution we can omit the μ and σ terms:

In[35]:= **PDF[NormalDistribution[], x]**

Out[35]= $\dfrac{e^{-\frac{x^2}{2}}}{\sqrt{2\pi}}$

Next, we plot the standard normal distribution by making use of its formula.

We specify a domain of −6 to 6:

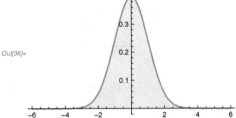

$\text{In[36]:=}\ \mathsf{Plot}[\dfrac{1}{\sqrt{2 * \pi * 1^2}} * \mathsf{Exp}[\dfrac{-(x^2)}{2 * 1^2}], \{x, -6, 6\}, \mathsf{Filling} \rightarrow \mathsf{Axis}]$

Out[36]=

This is exactly the same as using the NormalDistribution function:

$\text{In[37]:=}\ \mathsf{Plot}[\mathsf{PDF}[\mathsf{NormalDistribution}[], x], \{x, -6, 6\}, \mathsf{Filling} \rightarrow \mathsf{Axis}]$

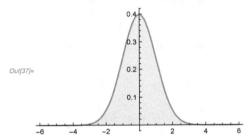

Out[37]=

Now that we have a good understanding of the normal distribution, we can simulate an experiment by taking samples for the measurement of a variable from a population in which the variable is normally distributed. Let's imagine that the variable has a mean of 100 and a standard deviation of 20 in the population. We will take 60 samples at random from this population for our experiment and store it in the computer variable sampleVariable.

Create a random sample of 60 cases from a normal distribution of 100 and a standard deviation of 20:

```
In[38]:= SeedRandom[123]
        sampleVariable = RandomVariate[NormalDistribution[100, 20], 60];
```

Your experiment will have a sample taken from a larger population. For the instance above, let's see what the random sample mean and standard deviation are.

The mean of the random sample:

```
In[40]:= Mean[sampleVariable]
```

Out[40]= 97.1044

The standard deviation of the random sample:

In[41]:= **StandardDeviation[sampleVariable]**

Out[41]= 19.9721

These values are close to 100 and 20. The question is, how close? As we learn about inferential statistics in the coming chapters, we will learn to express how different a statistic is from a stated value or how different two statistics for the same variable are between two groups.

Taking samples from populations and exploring and comparing different statistics for the variables under consideration are at the heart of inferential statistics. This is how we investigate our research questions. For example, we might randomly divide a sample taken from a larger population into two groups. One group receives an intervention and the other not. We then measure a variable for each subject in the two groups and compare the statistics for that variable between them. One of the most common statistics that we compare is the mean.

An important lesson is that we base our assumption on the distribution of the variable in the underlying population. When it comes to common tests, such as the Student t test, we must be sure of this assumption or else we will get inaccurate and misleading results. Different tests must be used for different distributions.

One obvious problem is that we do not often have data from a whole population. We have to make a calculated guess as to what it is. One of the distributions that will come to our rescue is the t distribution.

t Distribution

The t distribution is a commonly used distribution and is the basis for the Student t test. It is used when the variance of a variable in a population is unknown, as well as when the sample size is small.

The t distribution is dependent on a value known as *degrees of freedom*. Think of degrees of freedom in the following way. You have three numbers and their mean is 10. For the mean to remain 10, two of the values can fluctuate wildly, but this fixes the third. There are two degrees of freedom in this example, that is, three total elements in a single group. The degrees of freedom is simply calculated as $3 - 1 = 2$.

For a given value for degrees of freedom, ν, the PDF of the t distribution is as follows.

Use the Wolfram Language to write the PDF of the *t* distribution:

In[42]:= **PDF[StudentTDistribution[v], x]**

Out[42]= $\dfrac{\left(\frac{v}{x^2+v}\right)^{\frac{1+v}{2}}}{\sqrt{v}\ \text{Beta}\left[\frac{v}{2},\frac{1}{2}\right]}$

In the example below, we create two curves, one with 2 and one with 30 degrees of freedom:

In[43]:= **Plot[Table[PDF[StudentTDistribution[v], x], {v, {2, 30}}] // Evaluate, {x, −6, 6}, Filling → Axis]**

Out[43]=

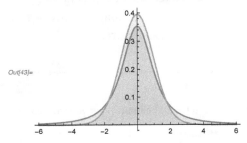

For smaller sample sizes (a lower value for degrees of freedom), there are more values in what is termed the *tails* of the distribution.

χ^2 Distribution

The χ^2 distribution is also dependent on degrees of freedom, v. It is the distribution of sums of squares of v values independently sampled from a normal distribution. It is a special case of the gamma distribution and is another one of the commonly used probability distributions used for the analysis of categorical variables.

We can use the ChiSquareDistribution function to plot the PDFs for a v of 2, 6, and 20.

Plot three χ^2 distributions:

In[44]:= **Plot[Table[PDF[ChiSquareDistribution[δ], x], {δ, {2, 6, 20}}] // Evaluate, {x, 0, 50}, Filling → Axis, PlotRange → All]**

Out[44]=

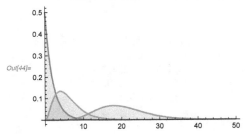

Below, we use the PDF function to express the formula for the χ^2 distribution.

The PDF for the χ^2 distribution in all its glory:

In[45]:= **PDF[ChiSquareDistribution[δ], x]**

Out[45]= $\begin{cases} \dfrac{2^{-\delta/2}\, e^{-x/2}\, x^{-1+\frac{\delta}{2}}}{\text{Gamma}\left[\frac{\delta}{2}\right]} & x > 0 \\ 0 & \text{True} \end{cases}$

These distributions and what they represent might seem esoteric at first. As you continue in this text, they will start making more sense. Refer back to this chapter often as your journey continues. The Wolfram Language contains many, many named distributions. Have a look at the documentation to learn more.

Exercises

8.1 Roll a hypothetical 10-sided die 10 000 times and save the result in the computer variable tenSidedDie.

8.2 Create a probability histogram of the results indicating the 10 values on the x axis.

8.3 Simulate the roll of two 10-sided dice for a total of 20 000 times. Store the List object in the computer variable tenSidedDice.

8.4 Create a computer variable named totals to hold the sum totals of each of the 20 000 rolls.

8.5 Create a probability density histogram of the totals List object.

8.6 What is the most likely total and what is the percentage probability of rolling it according to your plot?

8.7 Create a probability density plot of the standard normal distribution.

Tech Notes

- You can use a semicolon to suppress output to the screen, useful for large number outputs and longer strings of code. Try running the code below without the semicolon.

  SeedRandom[123]
  die = RandomInteger[{1, 6}, 10 000];

- Now try putting the semicolon back in and typing Short[%, 3] and then run the code again.

  Short[%, 3]

  {4, 6, 2, 3, 6, 1, 1, 3, 4, 2, 2, 5, 1, 2, 5, 4, 3, 3, 5, 6, 5, 3, 5, 2, 2, 5, 3, 1, 2, 2, 1, 6,
  5, 1, 5, 4, 2, 2, 3, 6, 5, 6, 2, 1, 6, 4, 6, 3, 4, 4, 2, 4, 2, 2, 6, 4, 2, 6, 3, 1, 2, 2, 3, 3, 5, 6,
  1, 4, 6, 3, 2, 6, 5, 6, 6, 3, 1, 6, 2, 1, 4, 5, ≪9836≫, 3, 2, 4, 3, 2, 4, 5, 1, 5, 5, 1, 2, 4, 2,
  2, 2, 5, 3, 5, 5, 5, 2, 3, 5, 3, 3, 5, 1, 6, 4, 2, 1, 3, 3, 3, 3, 1, 1, 6, 5, 3, 5, 3, 4, 1, 2, 3, 5,
  2, 3, 1, 3, 2, 3, 2, 2, 1, 6, 1, 5, 2, 1, 2, 1, 5, 2, 3, 2, 1, 2, 3, 4, 4, 4, 4, 3, 3, 3, 1, 5, 6, 2}

More to Explore

For fun, check out G. H. McClelland's manipulatable Wolfram Demonstration on normal distributions (wolfr.am/NormalDistribution)

Check out the Wolfram guide on normal and related distributions for more examples (wolfr.am/Distributions)

9 | Hypothesis Testing

We saw in the previous chapter that data point values for a variable come in various *patterns*. If we knew the value for a variable for every individual in a population, that would be great. As mentioned before, though, that is usually an impossible task. We, therefore, select a sample of individuals from a population and take measurements for a variable only for those individuals.

These individuals are not equal to the whole population. If we calculated the average for the set of data point values for a variable from our sample, chances are that it is going to be different from that of the population. A mean, median. variance, or standard deviation for a population is called a *parameter*, whereas the same values for a sample is called a *statistic*.

Not only will a specific statistic differ from its equivalent parameter, the very same statistic will also differ from sample to sample taken from the same population. We might walk into five different laboratories and take 10 sample values for the same variable under the exact same conditions. Chances are that all five laboratories will show slightly different statistics.

This brings home the point that whatever statistic we find for an experiment, it is but one of many, many possible statistics based on different samples taken from a population.

If we could do an experiment over and over and over again, we could actually build up a distribution of a specific statistic for a variable. Let's consider the mean as our prototypical statistic. We can indeed say that we will have a distribution of sample means over many similar experiments. This thought experiment leads us to the most important theory in inferential statistics, the central limit theorem.

Central Limit Theorem

Let's have a look at why this theorem is so important. Imagine that we could view the data point values for a variable over a whole population. Let's assume that the distribution of the data point values for this variable is uniform. It's like rolling a six-sided die, every value from one through six has the same probability of landing face up when the die is rolled.

Imagine then that we have 20 000 individuals and consider them a complete population. Imagine then further that a value for some variable is known for all 20 000 individuals. For the sake of explanation, the variable has a minimum value of 18 and a maximum value of 80 and is expressed as integer values. When selecting 20 000 values at random from this interval, each value has an equal likelihood of being selected.

We can use the Wolfram Language to generate these 20 000 values, storing them in the computer variable populationVar.

Create 20 000 data point values from a discrete uniform distribution:

```
In[1]:= SeedRandom[123];
        populationVar = RandomVariate[DiscreteUniformDistribution[{18, 80}], 20 000];
```

The equation for the mean value of a discrete uniform distribution for a variable x (populationVar in our case) is $\frac{1}{2}(x_{max} + x_{min})$. Since we created such a large population, our real mean (using the Mean function) will be very close to this.

Calculate the mean of our population:

```
In[3]:= Mean[populationVar] // N
```

```
Out[3]= 49.0548
```

Calculate the theoretical mean from our minimum and maximum values.

A space between the fraction and the opening parenthesis is shorthand for multiplication:

```
In[4]:= 1/2 (Max[populationVar] + Min[populationVar])
```

```
Out[4]= 49
```

We can make this supposition because we know it's a normal distribution and because the sample size is so large, but a histogram will show that we have a near discrete uniform distribution.

Specify a bin width of 1 and use Rule (→) to set labels and axes:

```
In[5]:= Histogram[populationVar, {1},
        PlotLabel → "Histogram of Our Variable", AxesLabel → {"Variable", "Count"}]
```

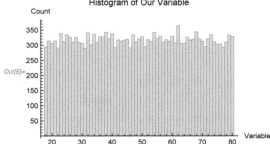

What will happen if we pick two random values from this population and calculate the average of those two values? What will a histogram of 25 of these means look like? In other words, what is the distribution of sample means? Note that our new data point values are for sample means!

You might be amazed to see that the distribution of sample means is not uniform. In fact, it is starting to resemble a normal distribution.

Create an empty List object and give it the computer variable name listMeans25:

In[6]:= **listMeans25 = List[];**

Using a simple Do loop, we'll create a block of code that will be repeated 25 times. Each iteration, two random values from populationVar will be selected randomly and their mean taken.

Then, we'll apply AppendTo to listMeans25, all in one line of code:

In[7]:= **SeedRandom[1234];**
Do[AppendTo[listMeans25, Mean[RandomChoice[populationVar, 2]]], 25]

Finally, create a histogram of the sampling means:

In[9]:= **Histogram[listMeans25, {10},**
PlotLabel → "Histogram of 25 Mean Values", AxesLabel → {"Mean", "Count"}]

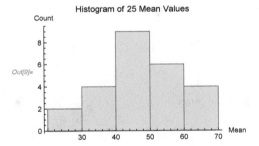

This process reflects what we do in real life when conducting research. We take individuals from a larger population and generate statistics such as a mean and a standard deviation. If we started our research one day later, we would have had a different sample set. So many things could influence each data point value.

The point we are repeating here is that whatever test statistic we calculate from a sample, it is but one of many that could have possibly occurred.

Let's carry on with our example to illustrate this further. Instead of taking two, we will take 30 individuals at random from our population and calculate the mean of those.

Repeat this 500 times and plot the histogram of all 500 sample means:

```
In[10]:= SeedRandom[1234]
listMeans500 = List[];
Do[AppendTo[listMeans500, Mean[RandomChoice[populationVar, 30]]], 500]
Histogram[listMeans500, {1},
    PlotLabel → "Histogram of 500 Mean Values", AxesLabel → {"Mean", "Count"}]
```

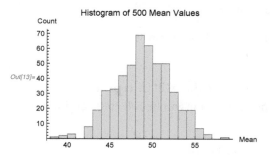

Low and behold, the sampling distribution of possible sample means is just about normally distributed, even when taking it from an original distribution that was not nearly normally distributed at all!

What you will also notice is that the mean of the sample means also starts to cluster around the actual population mean. When taking a sample of subjects from a population, it is much more common to get a mean from your sample that is close to the population mean than it is to get one that is very different. The probability of getting a mean far removed from the population mean actually becomes smaller.

Let's find the standard deviation of the small and large sample sizes.

Use the @ shorthand to apply the function to more than one List object using the //N postfix to return numerical values:

```
In[14]:= StandardDeviation/@{listMeans25, listMeans500} // N
```

```
Out[14]= {12.0292, 3.2132}
```

Notice how it is much smaller than the sampling standard deviation is for the larger number of sample means. When dealing with the standard deviation of the distribution of a statistic, we actually use the *standard error* and not the standard deviation. Standard error and standard deviation are usually quite similar; the difference is that standard deviation is calculated with the parameters of the population data and standard error uses statistics from the sample data. It is calculated as shown in the equation below.

$$\sigma_{\bar{x}} = \frac{\sigma}{\sqrt{n}}$$

It is simply the standard deviation divided by the square root of the sample size. Just for fun, let's calculate the mean and standard error of the sample means so that we can create a probability density curve. We will use the computer variables μ for the mean and **se** for the standard error.

Calculate the mean and standard error:

In[15]:= μ = Mean[listMeans500];
se = $\dfrac{\text{StandardDeviation[listMeans500]}}{\text{Sqrt[500]}}$;

Plot the distribution of the sample mean:

In[17]:= p = Plot[PDF[NormalDistribution[μ, se], x], {x, 48, 50}, Filling → Axis, PlotRange → All]

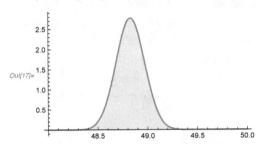

We are getting closer and closer to understanding inferential statistics. Let's put this knowledge of the central limit theorem to work by looking at confidence levels.

On the plot below, we overlay a density histogram of sample means with the probability density of NormalDistribution[μ, σ], where μ is equal to Mean[listMeans500] and σ is equal to StandardDeviation[listMeans500].

Note that AxesLabel assumes an *x, y* order for labeling:

In[18]:= Show[Histogram[listMeans500, Automatic, PDF,
        PlotLabel → "Histogram of 500 Mean Values", AxesLabel → {"Mean", "Count"}],
    Plot[PDF[NormalDistribution[μ, StandardDeviation[listMeans500]], x],
        {x, 38, 70}, Filling → Axis, PlotRange → All]]

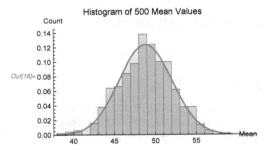

Confidence Levels

If you have read a research paper before, chances are that you have come across a confidence interval. Perhaps something like "The mean concentration of substance A was 30 mmol/L (95% CI 28.2–31.8 mmol/L)." The confidence level chosen in this example was 95%, resulting in the confidence interval of 28.2–31.8 mmol/L.

Confidence intervals are important in inferential statistics. In our example case, we are inferring that the mean from our sample can be used to represent the wider population. Therefore, anyone reading our results can use this information in their work. Why? Because a confidence of 95% is considered statistically sound if the researchers can demonstrate it.

We have to be careful of a subtle fact here. The 95% confidence interval of 28.2–31.8 mmol/L does not mean that we are 95% confident that the population mean falls between these two limits. What it actually means can be illustrated as follows. Imagine that we ran our experiment 100 times and every time we have a different sample, a different mean, and different limits for our confidence intervals. If each of these were calculated for a confidence level of 95%, 95 of the cases will actually have the population mean within the limits. When considering our single experiment, we cannot be sure that ours is one of the 95.

So, how do we calculate the confidence interval limits for a particular confidence level? As with all things in the Wolfram Language, it is not that difficult. It also gives us the opportunity to discuss the difference between a sampling distribution and the distribution of our sample.

Let's create a new population. We will once again imagine that there are only 20 000 subjects in this population. We will imagine that a variable that we are interested in has a normal distribution in the population. In the code that follows, we create the population, storing it in the computer variable populationVar2, and use the RandomChoice function to take a random sample of 30 subjects from the population.

Create a list of values for a variable in a population with a mean of 300 and a standard deviation of 15:

```
In[19]:= SeedRandom[123]
         populationVar2 = RandomVariate[NormalDistribution[300, 15], 20000];
```

Take 30 samples from our population but do not suppress the output:

```
In[21]:= SeedRandom[123]
         ourSample = RandomChoice[populationVar2, 30]
```

```
Out[22]= {269.31, 331.603, 313.009, 304.034, 302.543, 312.984, 309.772, 291.615, 273.66, 284.481,
          327.436, 280.701, 284.01, 327.414, 313.383, 310.453, 301.145, 310.822, 319.841, 333.712,
          291.763, 280.445, 307.132, 314.657, 301.403, 312.15, 290.942, 300.109, 282.829, 298.057}
```

Start with the Mean for our sample:

```
In[23]:= Mean[ourSample]
```

```
Out[23]= 302.714
```

We note the difference between our sample mean and the population mean. We wish to infer if this result will hold for the real population, which we know to be 300 since we were the creators of the population.

To do so, let's look at the standard deviation:

In[24]:= **StandardDeviation[ourSample]**

Out[24]= 17.1165

Visualize it using **Histogram** with a bin size of 10:

In[25]:= **Histogram[ourSample, {10},**
   PlotLabel → "Histogram of Our Sample", AxesLabel → {"Value", "Count"}]

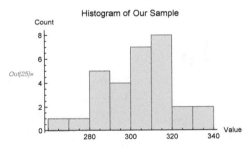

For the sake of illustrating the difference between the distribution of data point values in our sample and a sampling distribution, let's start by creating a SmoothHistogram of the sample.

SmoothHistogram requires a List (or saved data) to plot the PDF:

In[26]:= **SmoothHistogram[ourSample, Filling → Axis,**
   PlotLabel → "Smooth Histogram of Our Sample", AxesLabel → {"Value", "Count"}]

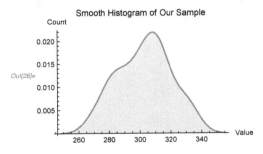

It is not a smooth bell-shaped curve, but it is certainly getting there. We can create a model distribution from our sample. This model distribution will be that of a sampling distribution. Instead of the standard deviation, it will use standard error to serve as the standard deviation parameter in the model.

Plot the model sampling distribution:

```
In[27]:= Plot[PDF[NormalDistribution[Mean[ourSample],
          StandardDeviation[ourSample]/Sqrt[30]], x], {x, 288, 320},
          Filling → Axis, PlotRange → All, PlotLabel → "Model Sampling Distribution"]
```

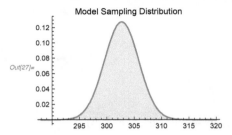

It is from this distribution that we can calculate the confidence interval values for a specific confidence level. To do so, we must import the Hypothesis Testing Package into the Wolfram Language. In the code cell below, we import this package using the Needs function. Downloading packages is nothing to be concerned about with the Wolfram Language. In fact, you've probably downloaded a few already just by using particular functions.

If you ever want to check on your paclets, palettes, and applications, use SystemOpen:

```
In[28]:= SystemOpen @ FileNameJoin[{$UserBaseDirectory, "Applications"}]
```

Take note of the quotation marks and the back tick at the end:

```
In[29]:= Needs["HypothesisTesting`"]
```

We can now use the MeanCI function to calculate the confidence intervals around our sample mean.

The default for MeanCI will calculate a 95% confidence interval:

```
In[30]:= MeanCI[ourSample]
```

```
Out[30]= {296.322, 309.105}
```

Specify other confidence levels:

```
In[31]:= MeanCI[ourSample, ConfidenceLevel → 0.8]
```

```
Out[31]= {298.616, 306.812}
```

You will notice that the limits are much narrower for a lower confidence level. When you read the next section about hypothesis testing and research questions, this will become clear. The confidence level of 95% represents 0.95 of the area under the curve of the probability distribution function (which is 1.0 in total). Centered from the middle of the curve, the confidence interval is worked out to cover 0.95 of the area under the curve. The limits are read off of the x axis. This tells you why a lower confidence level, such as 80%, has narrower limits. It simply covers less of the area under the curve.

We can illustrate the confidence intervals by drawing two vertical lines on the previous plot. First we create two computer variables to hold the lower and upper bound values with the confidence interval.

Create two computer variables to hold the CI values; use indexing to get the first and second values:

In[32]:= **{lb, ub} = MeanCI[ourSample]**

Out[32]= {296.322, 309.105}

The Epilog → Line argument will add lines between specified points:

In[33]:= **sampleDist =**
      NormalDistribution[Mean[ourSample], StandardDeviation[ourSample]/Sqrt[30]];
  lines = Line[{{{lb, 0}, {lb, 0.13}}, {{ub, 0}, {ub, 0.13}}}];
  Plot[PDF[sampleDist, x], {x, 288, 320}, Filling –> Axis,
    Ticks → {{{lb, "lb"}, {ub, "ub"}}, Automatic}, PlotRange –> All,
    PlotLabel –> "Theoretical Sampling Distribution with 95% CI",
    Epilog → {Dashed, lines}]

Out[35]=
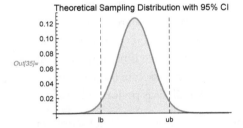

The next plot is a demonstration of the confidence intervals and the area under the curve:

In[36]:= **Plot[PDF[NormalDistribution[Mean[ourSample],**
      StandardDeviation[ourSample]/Sqrt[30]], x], {x, 288, 320}, Filling → Axis,
    PlotRange → All, PlotLabel → "Theoretical Sampling Distribution with 95% CI",
    Epilog → Line[{{{lb, 0}, {lb, 0.13}}, {{ub, 0}, {ub, 0.13}}}]]

Out[36]=
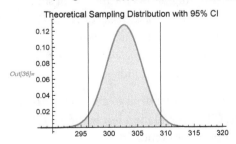

For a confidence level of 95%, we see 2.5% of the area of the curve to the left of the left vertical line and another 2.5% of the area to the right of the right vertical line.

This is exactly how we are going to calculate a *p*-value for a parametric test, i.e. for testing the difference in means between two samples. According to the central limit theorem, there can be any number of possible differences. We will calculate a statistic from our sample means and that will create the points on the *x* axis, creating the vertical lines. We can then calculate the area under the density curve from the lines toward either side, giving us a one-sided test *p*-value (or toward both ends for a two-sided test).

Hypothesis Testing and Research Questions

It's time to get a bit more rigorous. Our main interest in learning about statistics is to infer results from statistical tests performed on sample data to a larger population. We go through this exercise of taking samples from a population in such a way as to minimize any bias in the sample. Such bias might mean that our results are not transferable or generalizable, i.e. we cannot use the results as inference (extrapolate from the results of our sample and use it on the larger population).

Statistical tests are mathematical constructs (i.e. our sample means, distributions, and probability density curves) that provide a numerical solution to a research question. Think of these tests as using computation to calculate probabilities and then comparing those probabilities to meaningful threshold values. The research question is the fundamental building block of statistical analysis. It comes before any intervention takes place, before any data is collected, and most definitely before any data analysis is performed.

It is not correct to mine data for research questions and small *p*-values (high-confidence levels), but choosing too narrow a research question can result in a good deal of wasted resources if the results are completely out of the window of acceptability. A broader question with built-in follow ups will hopefully yield a more targeted approach where statistical certainty can be satisfied and the public trust maintained.

A research question has to be stated in a standard form that allows for the use of statistical tests. In inferential statistics, we call this standard form *hypothesis testing* or *testing the null hypothesis*. We can illustrate this through an example. Consider the question of whether there is a difference between the effect on blood pressure between two drugs. Let's run through an experiment to answer this question in our minds.

Such a question might stem from wondering about the correct drug to give to a certain population with hypertension (high blood pressure). The population is a set of people with hypertension. In a way that minimizes bias, a number of individuals are taken from that population. Testing the whole population is almost never feasible. Now individuals in the sample are randomly assigned to receive one of the two drugs. It is common for one of them to be a placebo, but that is not of interest here. Blood pressure readings are taken after treatment for all the individuals in the sample. We now need to evaluate if there was a difference in the mean blood pressures between the two groups.

Now that we have thought about the problem, we start by setting up our research question as a hypothesis. A hypothesis has two parts, called the *null* and the *alternative hypothesis*. The null hypothesis reflects our base belief, i.e. that there is no difference between the mean blood pressures of the two samples (groups). It is usually denoted as H_0. The alternative hypothesis states that there is a difference in the mean blood pressures between the two groups. We denote this as H_α.

Choosing the appropriate statistical test to compare the mean blood pressures between the two groups will result in a numerical value called the test statistic. You could well imagine that there are many possible values for this test statistic based on the blood pressure readings that were captured for the samples. If we started our experiment a week later, we might have ended up with a different set of individuals from the population. This difference in means that we calculate from our sample will be one of many possible differences. This should remind you of the central limit theorem.

What Is a p-Value?

Wolfram MathWorld states that the *p*-value is simply "the probability that a variate would assume a value greater than or equal to the observed value strictly by chance: $P(z \geq z_{\text{observed}})$."

As stated previously, the central limit theorem ensures that there will be a bell-shaped distribution of these possible differences in means, and ours will be one of them. According to the sampling distribution, some values (differences in means) will occur more commonly than others. We can set an arbitrary significance value, beyond which the value would occur very rarely. We convert this value to a probability (*p*-value) by calculating the area under the distribution curve beyond the cut-off (vertical) lines. The cut-off (or significance level) is called the α-value and is usually set at 0.05 (or 5%). If the probability is smaller than this, we call the difference between the groups statistically significant.

Consider this carefully, though. The distribution of possible test statistics is drawn up from the null hypothesis, i.e. that there is no difference between the two groups. Given that we accept that, in reality, there is no difference, if we then find a rare value, we say, given that there is no real difference, that we found a rare value and therefore reject our null hypothesis and accept the alternative hypothesis. We never actually prove that there is a difference. We simply say that given that there is no difference, we found a rare result. There is no way to set up a distribution that states as its base that there is a difference. The curve that is drawn from all the possible test statistics assumes that there is no difference! This is actually a bit hard to swallow when you first learn about it. A *p*-value is based on a mathematical curve that states that there is no difference. There is no magical power behind it and the significance level of 0.05 isn't magical either. It doesn't actually prove anything! In fact, many scholars and even journals are moving away from the use of *p*-values.

What Is the z Distribution?

Next is a plot of a standard normal sampling distribution drawn for 100 samples, with a mean of 0 and a standard error of 1. This is sometimes referred to as the z distribution, although the sample size is not relevant to that definition. It is also sometimes referred to as the "standard normal distribution." As described here, it is a model of all the possible test statistics, with 0 (no difference in means between the two groups) occurring most often. The test statistic for our difference will fall somewhere on the x axis. Remember that since we are dealing with computing a continuous variable probability, it makes more sense to calculate the area under the curve (p-value) between two points, as the probability of using a continuous random variable to obtain a specific value is zero.

Plot the curve from the test statistic toward its left and right tails:

In[37]:= **Plot[PDF[NormalDistribution[0, $\dfrac{1}{\text{Sqrt[100]}}$], x], {x, −0.5, 0.5},**
PlotRange → All, Filling → Axis, PlotLabel → "z Distribution for 100 Samples"]

Out[37]=

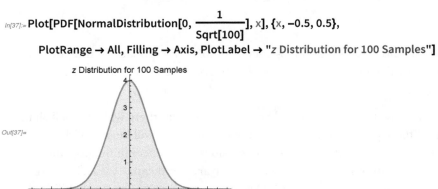

The Process of Hypothesis Testing

Below is an idealized image of the process. It represents a distribution of possible test statistics. The orange area under the curve is equal to 5% of the total area under the curve. The black line translates to a specific test statistic value on the x axis (difference between means). We will learn later how to transform our actual difference in means to this x axis value. For the p-value, we calculate the black area under the curve. It is clearly smaller than 5%, so we reject our null hypothesis and accept our alternative hypothesis, i.e. a statistically significant result.

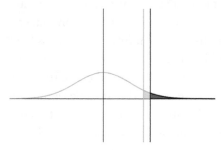

This is actually called a one-tailed test. We put all of our eggs in one basket, so to speak. The alternative hypothesis in this case would actually not state that there is a difference in the effect of the drug on blood pressure but that one is higher than the other, with the null hypothesis that it is equal to or lower than the placebo group. This form of hypothesis testing should rarely be used. It is only valid if we can convince ourselves and our peers that it was correct to hold such an assumption.

It is much more common to use the two-tailed approach, where we simply state the alternative hypothesis as there being a difference. This means we split our 5% area into two, i.e. 2.5% on either side. We also duplicate the black areas.

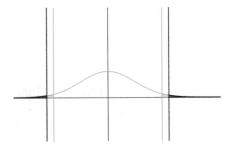

The reason why we duplicate the black line is easy to understand. It simply follows from the order in which we do the subtraction to calculate the difference in means. If the mean blood pressure in the first group was 110 mm Hg and in the second group it was 111 mm Hg, the difference could be either + 1 or − 1 depending on which group we place first.

Irrespective of which, we convert this difference into a value that we place on the x axis of this sampling distribution of all possible differences that is guaranteed by the central limit theorem. We duplicate it on the other side of the graph for a two-tailed test.

Since we are dealing with continuous variables, we stated that we can only calculate the area under the curve between values. The idea here is that we calculate the area on the curve from negative infinity to the x axis value on the left side and from the x axis value on the right to positive infinity. This is not too complicated and is accomplished using the cumulative distribution function.

A few things are important to reiterate. Any difference we find between statistics for two or more groups is but one of many possible differences that we could have found if we could run an experiment many times over.

Given the results at hand, we construct a distribution of sampling values (all the many possible outcomes) and place our specific value somewhere on this curve. Through calculating the area under the curve, this allows us to find out what the probability was of finding such a result, i.e. we calculate a p-value.

Cumulative Distribution Function

We have mentioned before that the total area under the curve of a PDF is 1 (representing 100%).

Let's take another look at the PDF of the standard normal distribution:

In[38]:= **Plot[PDF[NormalDistribution[], x], {x, −6, 6}, Filling → Axis]**

Out[38]=

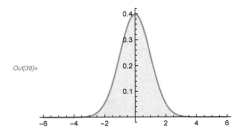

The area under the curve is actual calculated by the cumulative distribution function (CDF). It steps along the x axis from the left and starts adding the area under curve as it goes. Put differently, the value of a CDF at a point a is the area under the PDF from -∞ to a.

Let's look at a plot of the CDF for the standard normal distribution:

In[39]:= **Plot[CDF[NormalDistribution[], x], {x, −6, 6}, Filling → Axis, PlotRange → All]**

Out[39]=

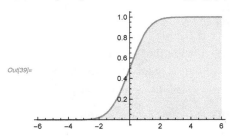

This is how the area under the curve for the black and orange lines in the previous plot are calculated. We can use it to simply read the area (p-value from the y axis for any given value on the x axis).

The area under the curve for an x value of −1.96:

In[40]:= **CDF[NormalDistribution[], −1.96]**

Out[40]= 0.0249979

So, if you look back up at the plot of the PDF and draw a line upwards at the x axis value of − 1.96, you will get about 0.025 (2.5%) of the area under the curve. What about + 1.96, though?

The area under the curve for an *x* value of +1.96:

In[41]:= **CDF[NormalDistribution[], 1.96]**

Out[41]= 0.975002

As the CDF adds from the left, a line drawn upwards from +1.96 will accumulate 0.975 (97.5%) of the area under the curve. This is not what we want. We need the area under the curve from this point onwards to the right. As we know that the total area is 1, we can simply subtract from 1.

Calculate the area under the curve for an *x* value of +1.96 toward the right:

In[42]:= **1 − CDF[NormalDistribution[], 1.96]**

Out[42]= 0.0249979

So, there you have it. The CDF calculates the actual area under the curve for a value on the *x* axis that we desire or, more precisely, from -∞ to a given value on the *x* axis. All that is left to do is to convert a difference in means (or other statistic) to a value that we can place on the *x* axis of the PDF plot. We will do this in the next chapter.

Exercises

9.1   Import the Hypothesis Testing Package.

9.2   Create a computer variable named **vals** to hold a List object containing 500 random values from a normal distribution with a mean of 100 and a standard deviation of 20.

9.3   Create a histogram of **vals** with a default bin size.

9.4   Create a smooth histogram of **vals** representing an idealized distribution and add a fill to the axis.

9.5   Calculate the 95% confidence interval for the mean of **vals**.

More to Explore

Check out this interactive Demonstration by C. Boucher all about hypothesis testing
(wolfr.am/PopulationMean)

For more information on Wolfram's Hypothesis Testing Package, see this tutorial
(wolfr.am/HypothesisTesting)

Wolfram Media author Seth Chandler provides a precise definition of the *p*-value
(wolfr.am/definition-P-value)

10 | Parametric Tests, Comparing Means

You are now ready to do some actual inferential statistical tests. Our aim with the rest of this text is to choose a statistical test and compute a test statistic. This statistic will fall somewhere on a curve of a PDF, and we can calculate a probability from this.

Assumptions about Parametric Tests

There are two general types of tests. They are *parametric* and *nonparametric* tests (more on the latter in Chapter 14). Parametric tests are much more commonly used. They include William Gosset's famous Student *t* test and analysis of variance (ANOVA).

Many assumptions are made when using these parametric tests, and it is important to know about them and to test the validity of your data against them before using these tests. Even if these assumptions are not met, you can still use parametric tests, but your results might not be trustworthy.

Parametric tests are more sensitive at picking up differences between means. A comparative nonparametric test might not pick up a difference. For example, the *p*-value when using a parametric test on data might be 0.044, and when using the nonparametric test on the same data, the *p*-value is 0.051, a very small but important difference. If the assumptions for the use of the parametric test were not met, it might be wrong to use it to announce a significant result.

The first assumption is that the data point values for a variable in a sample must have a normal distribution in the population from which the sample individuals where taken. This is a bit hard to know for sure since we almost never have data point values from the whole population. Luckily, there are various tests that we can use to infer this assumption based on the the data point values from our sample.

The first is a visual method, called a quantile-quantile (q-q) plot. It plots the quantiles of a list of data point values for a variable against a chosen distribution. In this case, we are interested in the normal distribution. In the next example we create two lists, one containing random values from the standard normal distribution and the other containing random samples from an χ^2 distribution, with one degree of freedom. The lists are stored in the computer variables stdNormalSample and chi2Sample. We then create two q-q plots. The Wolfram Language plotting function for q-q plots is QuantilePlot.

Use the list as the argument and the data distribution in which we are interested:

In[1]:= **SeedRandom[123]**
 stdNormalSample = RandomVariate[NormalDistribution[], 100];
 chi2Sample = RandomVariate[ChiSquareDistribution[1], 100];

Let's create a q-q plot for the stdNormalSample list (samples from a standard normal distribution) that we created against the quantiles of the standard normal distribution.

The first argument is the actual list object and the second is the distribution against which we are testing:

In[4]:= **QuantilePlot[stdNormalSample, NormalDistribution[]]**

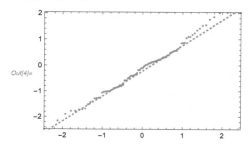

Now create a q-q plot against the quantiles of the standard normal distribution for the chi2Sample list created above:

In[5]:= **QuantilePlot[chi2Sample, NormalDistribution[]]**

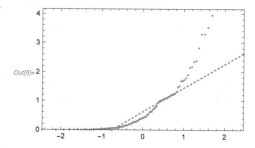

We see the obvious difference. In the first q-q plot, the data point values closely follow the straight line representing the standard normal distribution. Not so much the second. If these were the data point values for a variable from one of the groups in our experiment, we should not use a parametric test in its analysis.

The other methods for testing the assumption of normality are themselves statistical tests. One well-known test is the Shapiro–Wilk test. The null hypothesis states that the sample was taken from a population in which the data point values for that variable are normally distributed.

In the code cell below, we use the **ShapiroWilkTest** function. The first argument takes the list of values that we are testing. The second is one of a few arguments that regulates what we see on screen when the test is run. In this case, we will use **"TestDataTable"**, which will return a statistic (this is the value we place on the x axis of a sampling distribution plot) and the second is the p-value for that statistic.

Use **"TestDataTable"** to run the Shapiro–Wilk test on the normal list:

$In[6]:=$ **ShapiroWilkTest[stdNormalSample, "TestDataTable"]**

$Out[6]=$	Statistic	P-Value
Shapiro-Wilk	0.989048	0.58831

Since we created a list by taking random values from a standard normal distribution, we note a p-value that is not less than 0.05. We cannot reject the null hypothesis that this sample was taken from a population in which the data point values are normally distributed. For this set of data point values, we have met the assumption of normality and can use a parametric test (if the other assumptions that we discuss below are met).

As a side note, it is entirely possible to have drawn a sample using the **NormalDistribution** function that will have a p-value of less than 0.05. It is just rare.

As for the second list, which was data point values drawn from a non-normal distribution, we will see a p-value of less than 0.05. We can therefore reject the null hypothesis and accept the alternative hypothesis that the sample data was not from a population in which that variable is normally distributed. At this point, it would be incorrect to use a parametric statistical test.

Now let's run the same code for the chi2Sample list:

$In[7]:=$ **ShapiroWilkTest[chi2Sample, "TestDataTable"]**

$Out[7]=$	Statistic	P-Value
Shapiro-Wilk	0.618848	9.95542×10^{-15}

Other tests, such as the Kolmogorov–Smirnov test, also exist. You can learn more about it in the Documentation Center. We will use the q-q plot and Shapiro–Wilk test throughout the rest of this text.

The second assumption that we will test is whether statistical outliers exist. In general terms, we can view these values as those that are more than 1.5 times the interquartile range (IQR) more than the third quartile or less than the first quartile. Again, we have a visual method using a box-and-whisker chart. Using the **"Outliers"** argument plots suspected outliers.

First we will create a list, called mass, containing data point values for a random variable:

In[8]:= **mass = {107.6, 95.6, 94.3, 92.3, 90.7, 89.4, 88.8, 86.9, 85.8, 85.5, 84.4, 84.1, 82.5, 81.4,**
80.8, 80.8, 79., 79.5, 78.4, 78.4, 78.2, 78.1, 78.4, 77.4, 76.5, 75.4, 74.8, 74.1,
73.5, 73.2, 73., 72.3, 72.3, 72.2, 71.8, 71.7, 71.6, 71.6, 71.5, 71.3, 70.7, 70.6,
70.5, 69.2, 68.6, 68.3, 117.5, 67., 66.8, 66.1, 65.8, 65.6, 64.9, 64.6, 124.5, 64.5,
64.3, 64.2, 63.9, 63.7, 39.7, 62.3, 62.2, 29.4, 57.8, 57.8, 57.6, 56.4, 53.6, 53.2};

Below is a box-and-whisker plot of the mass variable:

In[9]:= **BoxWhiskerChart[mass, "Outliers"]**

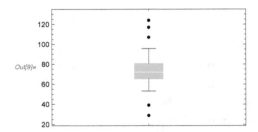

The dots in the plot above lie beyond the whiskers and are outliers.

There is also a numerical method that uses the standardized value for each data point value. It expresses how many standard deviations each value is from the mean. This can be achieved using the Standardize function. Any absolute value larger than 3.0 is suspected as being an outlier.

In the code cell below, we standardize each value using the Standardize function. This is wrapped in the Abs function that turns every value into a positive value. Finally, this is wrapped in Sort with the Greater function that will list the values in descending order (starting with the greatest value).

Use Sort and Abs to standardize values for each data point value sorted in descending order:

In[10]:= **Sort[Abs[Standardize[mass]], Greater]**

Out[10]= {3.41991, 3.0138, 2.94634, 2.31699, 2.27659, 1.46476, 1.40368, 1.37682, 1.37662, 1.24151,
1.1872, 1.13327, 1.10601, 1.09248, 1.09248, 1.04532, 1.00473, 0.876191, 0.801773,
0.794815, 0.78805, 0.781478, 0.707061, 0.693337, 0.686765, 0.679806, 0.659511, 0.652746,
0.639215, 0.63245, 0.612154, 0.578522, 0.564798, 0.551268, 0.530972, 0.504104, 0.483616,
0.470085, 0.463513, 0.463513, 0.382137, 0.375566, 0.361842, 0.34174, 0.321251, 0.301148,
0.301148, 0.301148, 0.287618, 0.280853, 0.233496, 0.233303, 0.226538, 0.219773,
0.179181, 0.172609, 0.165651, 0.158886, 0.158886, 0.15212, 0.145355, 0.118294,
0.111529, 0.111529, 0.0981921, 0.0641728, 0.0576009, 0.0506424, 0.0303468, 0.0102445}

We note that there are only two values that are more than three standard deviations from the mean. We can use the Select function to print only the values larger than 3. In the next piece of code, we omit the Abs function. Using the placeholder symbol, #, we look for values that are larger than 3 or less than −3. The ‖ function (shift \ on most keyboards) is the Wolfram Language code for "or," as in either of the two situations will satisfy a value or values returned to the screen.

Select all absolute values larger than 3 or less than −3 (Note the use of the placeholder variable # and the use of the & symbol):

In[11]:= **Select[Standardize[mass], # > 3 || # < −3 &]**

Out[11]= {3.41991, −3.0138}

The researcher must decide what to do with the statistical outliers. When they are omitted, it should be stated in the results of any report. Better still is the use of a nonparametric test, discussed in Chapter 14.

What We Want to Achieve

Parametric tests are used to compare the means of data point values of a continuous numerical variable between categorical groups. The groups are made up of the unique values for a categorical variable, also called the *independent variable*. The data type of the variable that is to be examined must be continuous and numerical and is called the *dependent variable*.

An example might be to compare the cholesterol levels (the dependent variable, which is continuous and numerical) between patients receiving three types of treatment. Here, the three treatments, i.e. *Treatment 1*, *Treatment 2*, and *Placebo*, are the unique data point values for a variable that we will name *Treatment* for the sake of clarity. It should be clear that *Treatment* is a nominal categorical variable (the independent variable).

The means of the cholesterol values for the three groups will be compared to each other using ANOVA. If we only had two groups, we would use the Student *t* test. If the groups were paired (i.e. before and after results), we would use a paired-sample *t* test. All of these are types of parametric tests.

In short, we use parametric tests to test a hypothesis. You can review Chapter 9 on hypothesis testing to refresh your memory. Parametric tests compare means, with the null hypothesis that there is no difference in means for a continuous numerical variable between our groups. The alternative hypothesis will then state that there is a difference (two-tailed). In a one-tailed test, the alternate hypothesis clearly states which difference (higher or lower) is intended.

Creating Lists to Work With

Before we conduct our first statistical tests, let's use the Wolfram Language to create data point values for our use. We will create three list objects of 30 data point values each for an arbitrary continuous numerical variable. Each of the list objects will be for a different group of subjects. We will use the computer variables groupA, groupB, and groupC to store the list objects.

Create three list objects to hold the data for the same variable for three different groups:

```
In[12]:= SeedRandom[123]
         groupA = RandomVariate[NormalDistribution[20, 5], 30];
         groupB = RandomVariate[NormalDistribution[27, 7], 30];
         groupC = RandomVariate[NormalDistribution[30, 8], 30];
```

Although these lists were created as simulated data following a normal distribution, we must get into the habit of testing the two main assumptions for the use of parametric tests. We will use both the q-q plot and the Shapiro–Wilk test. Since we are generating only 30 values, don't be alarmed when you run the code and find that the data does not form a normal distribution!

Generate a q-q plot for groupA against a normal distribution:

```
In[16]:= QuantilePlot[groupA, NormalDistribution[]]
```

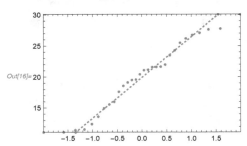

Now return just the *p*-value for groupA:

```
In[17]:= ShapiroWilkTest[groupA]
```

```
Out[17]= 0.217352
```

Do the same things for groupB and groupC:

```
In[18]:= QuantilePlot[groupB]
```

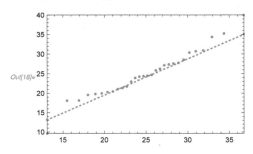

```
In[19]:= ShapiroWilkTest[groupB]
```

```
Out[19]= 0.596399
```

In[20]:= **QuantilePlot[groupC]**

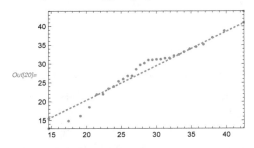

Out[20]=

In[21]:= **ShapiroWilkTest[groupC]**

Out[21]= 0.471446

Now let's look for statistical outliers using a box-and-whisker plot:

In[22]:= **BoxWhiskerChart[{groupA, groupB, groupC},**
   "Outliers", ChartLabels → {"Group A", "Group B", "Group C"}]

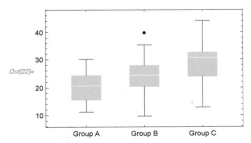

Out[22]=

We can also use the method of expressing the standardized value for each list. In the code below, we use 3 and −3 as our cut-off values as before.

The Table function is used to iterate through all three of our List objects:

In[23]:= **Table[Select[Standardize[n], # > 3 || # < −3 &], {n, {groupA, groupB, groupC}}]**

Out[23]= {{}, {}, {}}

The One-Sample Test

Our first statistical test will be a simple one-sample test based on the standard normal sampling distribution, where the standard error is 1. This is often called the z distribution. We will use groupA in this example. Imagine that these were values obtained from adding test reagents to a new piece of laboratory equipment. It is claimed that the test samples should give an average value of 20.

First, we note our sample mean:

In[24]:= **Mean[groupA]**

Out[24]= 20.0277

The question is: Is the claim valid? Validity here might describe whether the equipment is accurate. Our null hypothesis will be that there is no difference between the sample mean and the claimed mean of 20. Let's set an α-value of 0.05 to discriminate between a significant and nonsignificant result. Remember, we will build a distribution of all possible sample means based on the *fact in reality* that there is no difference. If our difference is one of the rare ones, we reject the null hypothesis and accept the alternate hypothesis.

Let's calculate the difference in means:

In[25]:= **Mean[groupA] − 20**

Out[25]= 0.0277016

Change the order of subtraction:

In[26]:= **20 − Mean[groupA]**

Out[26]= −0.0277016

Now for the big question: How do we use this difference to find out where on the z distribution's x axis this value lies so that we can calculate a p-value?

Well, we convert this difference into a z-score (units of standard error). There is something special about this example that we have not discussed before. In order to carry on, we must know the standard deviation of the test reagents that were used in the experiment. This does not refer to the standard deviation of the sample but for the population. Remember that we are looking into a new piece of laboratory equipment. This is not known. Usually, though, when we have a sample size of greater than 30, we can use the sample standard deviation as a stand-in for the population standard deviation. Remember that standard error was the ratio (division) between the sample standard deviation (in the numerator) and the square root of the sample size (in the denominator).

Calculate the standard error:

In[27]:= **se =** $\dfrac{\textbf{StandardDeviation[groupA]}}{\textbf{Sqrt[Length[groupA]]}}$

Out[27]= 1.01653

The z-score, in units of error, is the difference in means divided by the standard error:

In[28]:= **z =** $\dfrac{\textbf{Mean[groupA] − 20}}{\textbf{se}}$

Out[28]= 0.0272512

This is the mark on the *x* axis. We can calculate the *p*-value using the CDF function. Remember the following: if your *z*-score is less than zero, use CDF. If it is more than zero, use 1 – CDF. Lastly, since this was a two-tailed test, we multiply the answer by 2 to get the *p*-value.

Note that the CDF function calculates from the left (negative infinity) side:

In[29]:= **(1 – CDF[NormalDistribution[], z]) * 2**

Out[29]= 0.978259

Since we are using the Wolfram Language, there is an easier way to do this. We use the LocationTest function. Below we specify that we want the solution in LocationTest → "TestDataTable" form and that we require the *z* distribution.

The first argument of the LocationTest function is the list object, the second is the mean against which we are testing, and the third contains the type of result we want:

In[30]:= **LocationTest[groupA, 20, {"TestDataTable", "Z"}]**

Out[30]=

	Statistic	P-Value
Z	0.0272512	0.978259

The LocationTest function actually allows for testing using more than just the *z* distribution. Here is the full list.

To return all the statistical tests available:

In[31]:= **LocationTest[groupA, 20, {"TestDataTable", All}]**

Out[31]=

	Statistic	P-Value
Paired T	0.0272512	0.978446
Paired Z	0.0272512	0.978259
Sign	16	0.855536
Signed-Rank	238.	0.918089
T	0.0272512	0.978446
Z	0.0272512	0.978259

We will cover some of these tests in the next section.

Comparing the Means of Two Samples

While it is fun to look at a single sample group, our aim is to compare the means of two groups. Just as the single sample mean had a sampling distribution (we used the *z* distribution above), so does the difference in means. In fact, if you consider the existence of many different means for different samples taken from a population, you can imagine that choosing two groups of samples and subtracting the mean of one group from the other will also give us a sampling distribution of differences.

Let's consider just such an example. We will use our groupA and groupB List objects. Both sample sizes are larger than 30, and the distribution will actually approximate the z distribution even though we do not know the population mean and standard deviation for the particular variable.

The differences between the calculations we have to consider here and for the one-sample above are minor. Instead of subtracting the given mean (20 in our prior one-sample test) from the sample mean, we simply subtract the mean of one sample from the other. The standard error is a bit more complicated, though, and is given in equation (1).

$$\text{se} = \sqrt{\frac{\sigma_1^2}{n_1} + \frac{\sigma_2^2}{n_2}} \tag{1}$$

Here, σ_1^2 and n_1 are the variance and sample count for one group and σ_2^2 and n_2 are the variance and sample count for the other group.

If our null hypothesis is that there is no difference between the groups, we can calculate the z-statistic as the difference between the means of the two groups divided by the standard error.

Calculate the standard error and the z-statistic:

```
In[32]:= se = Sqrt[(Variance[groupA]/Length[groupA]) + (Variance[groupB])/Length[groupB]];

z = Abs[(Mean[groupA] - Mean[groupB])/se]
```

```
Out[33]= 3.27443
```

If we swapped the order of the two groups around, we would have calculated a similar z-statistic but with the opposite sign. To calculate a p-value, remember to use CDF when the test statistic value is negative and 1 − CDF when it is positive. The alternative is to always use 1 − CDF and the absolute value of the z-statistic for two-tailed hypothesis testing (as was used in the code above). The code below shows a p-value that is less than an α-value of 0.05, and we can reject the null hypothesis.

The standard form for two-tailed alternative hypothesis testing, multiplying by 2:

```
In[34]:= (1 − CDF[NormalDistribution[], z]) * 2
```

```
Out[34]= 0.00105874
```

To make life easier, we can always use the LocationTest function. In the next code cell, we note three arguments. The first is a list (in curly braces) that contains the two list objects. The second is 0. It indicates that our null hypothesis states that there is no difference between the means. The third argument allows us to specify the test we would like performed.

If you look at the Z entry, you will note that it is exactly what we calculated previously:

In[35]:= **LocationTest[{groupA, groupB}, 0, {"TestDataTable", All}]**

Out[35]=

	Statistic	P-Value
Mann-Whitney	253.	0.00350117
Paired T	-2.99922	0.00550986
Paired Z	-2.99922	0.00270669
Sign	7	0.00522288
Signed-Rank	94.	0.00453359
T	-3.27443	0.00178834
Z	-3.27443	0.00105874

The Mann–Whitney, sign, and signed rank tests that you see in the table are all nonparametric tests.

This example used the fact that we had a relatively large sample size so that we could use the z distribution. This allowed us to substitute the population standard deviations with the sample standard deviations. However, we use the t distribution generally, especially when the sample sizes are smaller. This brings us to the Student t test.

Student t Test

We came across the t distribution in Chapter 8. It has the following PDF for degrees of freedom represented by δ.

The PDF for the t distribution:

In[36]:= **PDF[StudentTDistribution[δ], x]**

Out[36]= $\dfrac{\left(\frac{\delta}{x^2+\delta}\right)^{\frac{1+\delta}{2}}}{\sqrt{\delta}\ \text{Beta}\left[\frac{\delta}{2}, \frac{1}{2}\right]}$

Below we plot it for 28 degrees of freedom:

In[37]:= **Plot[PDF[StudentTDistribution[28], x],**
    {x, −6, 6}, Filling → Axis, PlotLabel → "The t distribution"]

Out[37]=

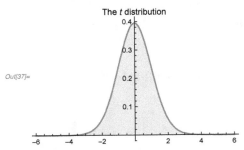

This distribution, when used for the Student t test, is also a representation of all possible differences in means between two groups. We use it when the sample sizes are small, i.e. we cannot substitute the sample standard deviation for the unknown population standard deviation to calculate standard error. This distribution requires a different set of equations. Let's take a look at them. The first equation of note is the *pooled standard deviation* of the two groups and is shown in (2) below.

$$s_p = \sqrt{\frac{(n_1 - 1)\, s_1^2 + (n_2 - 1)\, s_2^2}{n_1 + n_2 - 2}} \tag{2}$$

Again, the n_i values refer to the sample sizes of each of the two groups and the s_i^2 values are the corresponding group variances for i being 1 and 2. From this, we estimate the standard error for our sampling distribution, shown in equation (3).

$$se = s_p \sqrt{\frac{1}{n_1} + \frac{1}{n_2}} \tag{3}$$

Assuming that the null hypothesis is that there is no difference between the two groups, we calculate the *t*-statistic, which is simply the difference between the two means divided by the standard error.

$$t = \frac{\overline{x}_1 - \overline{x}_2}{se} \tag{4}$$

Here, $\overline{x}_1$ and $\overline{x}_2$ are the means of each group. Imagine that our List objects, groupA and groupB, represent data point values for a variable.

Let's look at the mean for each group:

In[38]:= **Mean[groupA]**

Out[38]= 20.0277

In[39]:= **Mean[groupB]**

Out[39]= 24.9343

In the code cell below, we calculate the pooled standard deviation and the standard error using the computer variables sp and se. The sample sizes for groups A and B are saved as nA and nB.

Calculate the pooled standard deviation using equations (2) and (3) above:

In[40]:= **nA = Length[groupA];**
nB = Length[groupB];
sp = $\sqrt{}$(((nA−1)∗Variance[groupA]+(nB−1)∗Variance[groupB])/(nA+nB−2));
se = sp∗$\sqrt{}$($\frac{1}{nA}$ + $\frac{1}{nB}$)

Out[43]= 1.49845

We can now calculate the *t*-statistic using equation (4). In this case, we will use the absolute value of the difference, forcing us to use $1 - $ CDF when calculating the *p*-value.

Calculate the *t*-statistic:

In[44]:= $t = Abs[\dfrac{Mean[groupA] - Mean[groupB]}{se}]$

Out[44]= 3.27443

Now we need the degrees of freedom. It is the sum of the sample sizes minus the number of groups:

Calculate the degrees of freedom:

In[45]:= $df = nA + nB - 2;$

Finally, we calculate the *p*-value using $1 - CDF$ for the StudentTDistribution. We multiply by 2 to get the two-tailed *p*-value. The CDF function takes two arguments. The first is the particular distribution and its appropriate argument(s) and the second is the test statistic, which we saved as t above).

Calculate the two-tailed *p*-value:

In[46]:= $(1 - CDF[StudentTDistribution[df], t]) * 2$

Out[46]= 0.00178834

For a chosen α-value of 0.05, we can reject the null hypothesis and state that there is a significant difference between the groups.

As you might have predicted, we can spare ourselves all of this headache and use the TTest function. It is important, though, to go through the calculations the long way at least once. It gives you a good feel for the *t* test.

As arguments to the TTest function, we pass the two list objects (representing the data point values for a variable for each of the two groups):

In[47]:= **TTest[{groupA, groupB}]**

Out[47]= 0.00178834

The TTest function can admit more arguments. Below we pass a 0 to indicate that our null hypothesis states that there is no difference between the groups. When we omit the 0, the Wolfram Language assumes a difference of 0.

We also specify **"TestDataTable"** and **"T"** to indicate that we want the test statistic and the *p*-value for the Student *t* test.

Use the LocationTest function:

In[48]:= **LocationTest[{groupA, groupB}, 0, {"TestDataTable", "T"}]**

Out[48]=

	Statistic	P-Value
T	-3.27443	0.00178834

We can also stipulate that our alternative hypothesis should be one tailed. The Less argument indicates that the first listed group has a mean smaller than the second listed group. Note that it is exactly half of the original *p*-value!

The one-tailed test for group A is less than that of group B:

In[49]:= **TTest[{groupA, groupB}, AlternativeHypothesis → "Less"]**

Out[49]= 0.00089417

The Wolfram Language allows us to create a TTest object, which has many properties that we can investigate. Below we create this object. By the way, you can get the $\mathcal{H}$, which we use for our computer variable, by typing esc scH esc .

Create a HypothesisTestData object for repeated property extraction:

In[50]:= $\mathcal{H}$ = **TTest[{groupA, groupB}, Automatic, "HypothesisTestData"]**

Out[50]= HypothesisTestData[➕ 〽️ Type: TTest
p–Value: 0.00179]

Clicking the ➕ sign in the output will reveal extra information about the object. The object has many properties that we can see listed using "**Properties**".

List the properties of the object:

In[51]:= $\mathcal{H}$**["Properties"]**

Out[51]= {DegreesOfFreedom, HypothesisTestData, Properties, PValue,
PValueTable, ShortTestConclusion, T, TestConclusion, TestData,
TestDataTable, TestEntries, TestStatistic, TestStatisticTable}

We can access them by simply stating them as arguments. You will note that the "**TestDataTable**" argument that we have been using is one of the properties. Let's have a look as some other properties of interest.

"**DegreesOfFreedom**" for a two-sample *t* test equates to the sum total of data point values minus the number of groups:

In[52]:= $\mathcal{H}$**["DegreesOfFreedom"]**

Out[52]= 58

The "**PValueTable**" argument returns only the *p*-value:

In[53]:= $\mathcal{H}$**["PValueTable"]**

Out[53]=

	P-Value
T	0.00178834

For "**ShortTestConclusion**", the default α-value is 0.05. When used in a table, it is useful to see one quick value rather than the longer "**TestConclusion**".

Use the "ShortTestConclusion" property:

In[54]:= $\mathcal{H}$["ShortTestConclusion"]

Out[54]= Reject

Simply using the "T" argument returns the *p*-value for the *t* test.

Return only the *p*-value:

In[55]:= $\mathcal{H}$["T"]

Out[55]= 0.00178834

The "TestConclusion" argument is particularly helpful if we are considering writing a report.

The "TestConclusion" argument returns a response to the statistic and *p*-value in sentence form:

In[56]:= $\mathcal{H}$["TestConclusion"]

Out[56]= The null hypothesis that the mean difference is 0
         is rejected at the 5 percent level based on the T test.

The "TestData" argument returns the *t*-statistic and the *p*-value as a List object.

The "TestData" argument returns a List object:

In[57]:= $\mathcal{H}$["TestData"]

Out[57]= {−3.27443, 0.00178834}

The "TestDataTable" argument returns the same information as above but formats it in an easy-to-read table:

In[58]:= $\mathcal{H}$["TestDataTable"]

Out[58]=

	Statistic	P-Value
T	-3.27443	0.00178834

"TestStatistic" and "TestStatisticTable" return only the *t*-statistic:

In[59]:= $\mathcal{H}$["TestStatistic"]

Out[59]= −3.27443

In[60]:= $\mathcal{H}$["TestStatisticTable"]

Out[60]=

	Statistic
T	-3.27443

All of these arguments are available for many other Wolfram Language statistical tests. As mentioned, the default α-value is 0.05. This can be changed at any time. In the code below, we create a HypothesisTestData object and set the α-value to 0.01.

Use the SignificanceLevel option:

In[61]:= $\mathcal{H}$ = TTest[{groupA, groupB}, 0, "HypothesisTestData", SignificanceLevel → 0.01];
$\mathcal{H}$["TestConclusion"]

Out[62]= The null hypothesis that the mean difference is 0
is rejected at the 1. percent level based on the T test.

The equation for the *t*-statistic and *p*-value is slightly different if there is an apprecia-tive difference between the variance of the two groups. If there is, this becomes the *t* test assuming unequal variances.

We can use the Wolfram Language to test for unequal variance:

In[63]:= TTest[{groupA, groupB}, 0, VerifyTestAssumptions → "EqualVariance"]

Out[63]= 0.00178834

The Paired-Sample *t* Test

For the sake of completeness, we will also take a look at the paired-sample *t* test. The paired-sample *t* test is used when there is dependence between the two groups. Using a set of subjects and measuring the same variable before and after an intervention in each of them serves as a good example. The *before* and *after* data point values now form the two groups. Each pair of values comes from the same individual and cannot be considered independent.

Below, we create two lists named **beforeIntervention** and **afterIntervention** to simulate an experiment where values for the same variable were collected before and after an intervention. Think of cholesterol values taken before and after starting a new drug that is hypothesized to lower blood cholesterol values. (A total blood cholesterol level above 240 mg/dL is considered high.)

SeedRandom recalls our earlier dataset, and before/after intervention variables are defined:

In[64]:= SeedRandom[123]
beforeIntervention = RandomVariate[NormalDistribution[240, 20], 30];
afterIntervention = RandomVariate[NormalDistribution[230, 35], 30];
Mean[afterIntervention] − Mean[beforeIntervention]

Out[67]= −20.4394

We note a fall in cholesterol of 20.4 mg/dL. Is there a significant difference between cholesterol level before and after initiating the new treatment (intervention)?

Although the lists were created taking random sample values from a normal distribution, it is good practice to check on our assumptions.

Below, we use the Shapiro–Wilks test and then create a box-and-whisker plot:

In[68]:= **ShapiroWilkTest[beforeIntervention]**

Out[68]= 0.217352

In[69]:= **ShapiroWilkTest[afterIntervention]**

Out[69]= 0.596399

In[70]:= **BoxWhiskerChart[{beforeIntervention, afterIntervention}, "Outliers"]**

Out[70]=
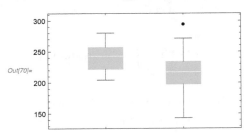

It seems that we can use the paired-sample *t* test.

The PairedTTest function is used to conduct this test:

In[71]:= **PairedTTest[{beforeIntervention, afterIntervention}, 0, "TestDataTable"]**

Out[71]=

	Statistic	P-Value
Paired T	2.74475	0.0102844

A "HypothesisTestData" object can be created for this test as well.

Create a "HypothesisTestData" object to extract all the properties used for the Student *t* test:

In[72]:= **𝓗 =**
　　PairedTTest[{beforeIntervention, afterIntervention}, Automatic, "HypothesisTestData"]

Out[72]= HypothesisTestData

Below is a list of the properties:

In[73]:= **𝓗["Properties"]**

Out[73]= {DegreesOfFreedom, HypothesisTestData, PairedT, Properties,
PValue, PValueTable, ShortTestConclusion, TestConclusion, TestData,
TestDataTable, TestEntries, TestStatistic, TestStatisticTable}

With a *p*-value of 0.01, we can reject the null hypothesis (for an α-value of 0.05) and state that there is a significant difference in the blood cholesterol value before and after taking the new medication. Since the mean cholesterol levels were lower after the treatment, we can conclude that the drug is probably effective.

Analysis of Variance

Analysis of variance (ANOVA) can be used to compare the means of more than two groups. For our purposes, let's use the three groups that we created at the start of this chapter.

Currently, the Wolfram Language does not have a function to conduct an analysis of variance test in a similar way as the TTest and PairedTTest that we used previously.

There is an external software package that can be imported into a notebook that does provide an ANOVA function, though. It takes a single line of code to import the package and we will do so at the end of this section.

To get a better understanding of ANOVA, we will start off this section by manually computing a statistic, in this instance an F-statistic, and a *p*-value.

Our first step in calculating the test statistic and the *p*-value using ANOVA is to calculate the variation within each sample, known as the *sum of squares within*. The is shown in equation (5) below.

$$\text{ssw} = \sum_{i=1}^{k}(n_i - 1)\, s_i^2 \tag{5}$$

Here, *n* is the number of samples in a specific group and s^2 is the variance of that group. Equation 5 is performed on each group and then the totals are summed.

First, we store the sample size of group C as nC:

In[74]:= **nC = Length[groupC];**

Length returns the number of items in a list. We will save this in the computer variable ssw:

In[75]:= **ssw = (nA − 1) ∗ Variance[groupA] + (nB − 1) ∗ Variance[groupB] + (nC − 1) ∗ Variance[groupC]**

Out[75]= **3426.17**

Now we calculate the mean of all the values.

First, clear any data remaining from our last session:

In[76]:= **Clear[data]**

Concatenate all three List objects as a nested List object and store it in the variable data:

In[77]:= **data = {groupA, groupB, groupC};**

Next up, we flatten the List object with the Flatten function. This will create one single list of all the data points values, which we will name **all**.

Flatten the data computer variable to a single List object:

In[78]:= **all = Flatten[data];**

This allows us to calculate the overall mean. Let's call the computer variable allMean.

Save the mean:

In[79]:= **allMean = Mean[all]**

Out[79]= **24.5091**

Next, we calculate the *sum of squares between* the groups. The is shown in equation (6).

$$\text{ssb} = \sum_{i=1}^{k} n_i \, (\overline{x}_i - \overline{x})^2 \tag{6}$$

Here, $\overline{x}_i$ is the mean of the group and $\overline{x}$ the is overall mean. This is done for each of the groups and then totaled. Below, we store it in the computer variable ssb.

Calculate the sum of squares between groups and save it in the computer variable ssb:

In[80]:= **ssb = nA * (Mean[groupA] − allMean)² +**
nB * (Mean[groupB] − allMean)² + nC * (Mean[groupC] − allMean)²

Out[80]= **1101.48**

Now we calculate the total sum of squares, which is the sum of the squares within and the sum of squares between.

We'll use the computer variable sst:

In[81]:= **sst = ssw + ssb**

Out[81]= **4527.65**

Next up is the *mean square between*. This is shown in equation (7).

$$\text{msb} = \frac{\text{ssb}}{k - 1} \tag{7}$$

Then we need the *mean square within*. Here, k is the number of groups. This is shown in equation (8).

$$\text{msw} = \frac{\text{ssw}}{N - k} \tag{8}$$

Here, N is the total number of data point values. Below, we use the computer variables msb and msw to hold these two calculations.

Equations (7) and (8) are implemented next.

Calculate the mean square between and save it in the computer variable msb:

In[82]:= **msb = $\dfrac{\text{ssb}}{3 - 1}$**

Out[82]= **550.742**

Calculate the mean square within and save it in the computer variable msw:

In[83]:= **msw = ssw / (nA + nB + nC − 3)**

Out[83]= 39.3813

Finally, we have the F-statistic, which is the ratio of the mean square within and the mean square between values. The purpose of the F-statistic is to find out if the means between populations are significantly different.

Calculate the F-statistic and save it in the computer variable f:

In[84]:= $f = \dfrac{msb}{msw}$

Out[84]= 13.9849

Since this is a statistic that falls on the F distribution (which we have not seen before), we can calculate a *p*-value from this. The FRatioDistribution function takes two arguments. The first is the number of groups minus one and the second is the total number of samples minus the number of groups. In our case, this would be 3 − 1 and 90 − 3.

We will use 1 − CDF to calculate the *p*-value:

In[85]:= **(1 − CDF[FRatioDistribution[3 − 1, 90 − 3], f])**

Out[85]= 5.41634×10^{-6}

For a chosen α-value of 0.05, we have a significant result. This means that there is a difference in the mean between the three groups. Note that there is no information here about where (between which of the three groups) this difference is.

If we draw a smooth histogram, we can visualize suspected differences between the groups:

In[86]:= **SmoothHistogram[{groupA, groupB, groupC},**
      PlotLegends → {"Group A", "Group B", "Group C"}]

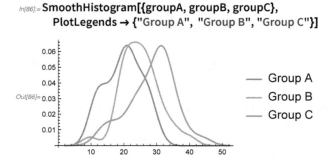

If the *p*-value is lower than the chosen α-value, we can do *post hoc* analysis comparing each pair of groups to find between which groups the differences are. Note that if the *p*-value was not smaller than our chosen α-value, we can still do *post hoc* analysis, but this is improper and should not be reported even if it shows significant differences between pairs of groups.

Now for the easy way, using the add-on package. The ANOVA Package can calculate the F-statistic and p-value so that we do not have to perform the calculations above.

We import the package using the Needs function. Remember to include the back tick:

In[87]:= **Needs["ANOVA`"]**

In the example above, we had three groups, A, B, and C (the independent variables). We need to prepare a nested list, such that each subList is of the following form: {*group, value*}, so for *group A*, we might have {1, 21}. Each data point value must be preceded by its group value.

We begin this list using the Table function:

In[88]:= **table = {Table[{1, groupA[[n]]}, {n, 30}],**
   Table[{2, groupB[[n]]}, {n, 30}], Table[{3, groupC[[n]]}, {n, 30}]}

Out[88]= {{{1, 26.2077}, {1, 19.1295}, {1, 21.6617}, {1, 19.5979}, {1, 12.435}, {1, 21.6059},
   {1, 11.1145}, {1, 27.7699}, {1, 21.1671}, {1, 13.6082}, {1, 11.485}, {1, 11.1281},
   {1, 26.7492}, {1, 24.2961}, {1, 21.9865}, {1, 21.6247}, {1, 27.0985}, {1, 16.0164},
   {1, 27.6307}, {1, 25.5132}, {1, 14.9582}, {1, 23.5086}, {1, 19.5237}, {1, 21.102},
   {1, 18.5806}, {1, 30.082}, {1, 17.6369}, {1, 15.5864}, {1, 11.5934}, {1, 20.4334}},
  {{2, 19.8517}, {2, 24.7173}, {2, 21.7825}, {2, 20.3383}, {2, 24.3923}, {2, 18.1237},
   {2, 28.6176}, {2, 25.8829}, {2, 24.5044}, {2, 24.2863}, {2, 18.1821}, {2, 30.7314},
   {2, 19.6031}, {2, 27.7974}, {2, 40.0368}, {2, 23.9422}, {2, 9.6427}, {2, 27.4077},
   {2, 35.2655}, {2, 27.6427}, {2, 34.3785}, {2, 30.9674}, {2, 21.1242}, {2, 20.5053},
   {2, 23.0077}, {2, 20.0276}, {2, 21.3936}, {2, 30.4082}, {2, 27.1769}, {2, 26.2905}},
  {{3, 28.6037}, {3, 44.1051}, {3, 24.0249}, {3, 37.014}, {3, 21.9396}, {3, 29.7677},
   {3, 23.4507}, {3, 35.1932}, {3, 38.81}, {3, 26.8593}, {3, 18.5571}, {3, 33.2112},
   {3, 31.1213}, {3, 34.5449}, {3, 26.0172}, {3, 14.845}, {3, 31.5317}, {3, 31.2477},
   {3, 32.5102}, {3, 12.8194}, {3, 21.9976}, {3, 30.2296}, {3, 31.5693}, {3, 16.1927},
   {3, 25.3961}, {3, 32.2106}, {3, 34.0102}, {3, 26.8273}, {3, 31.0684}, {3, 31.2822}}}}

As we can see, this created a nested list object of the desired format of {*group, value*} pairs, but each group is still nested in its own subList. This is corrected using the Flatten function, setting the level to 1.

This new list is stored as anovaTable below:

In[89]:= **anovaTable = Flatten[table, 1];**

We now have a list object with 90 pairs of values (sublists), each containing the group value and the variable value:

In[90]:= **Dimensions[anovaTable]**

Out[90]= {90, 2}

To make sure, we can take a look at three samples:

In[91]:= **anovaTable[[{1, 32, 75}]]**

Out[91]= {{1, 26.2077}, {2, 24.7173}, {3, 26.0172}}

The ANOVA function takes the list as argument and provides us with a table of results including the F-statistic, a p-value, and all the groups means starting with the overall mean.

Use the ANOVA function with the data in the correct format:

In[92]:= **ANOVA[anovaTable]**

Out[92]= $\left\{\text{ANOVA} \rightarrow\right.$

	DF	SumOfSq	MeanSq	FRatio	PValue
Model	2	1101.48	550.742	13.9849	5.41634×10^{-6}
Error	87	3426.17	39.3813		
Total	89	4527.65			

,

$\text{CellMeans} \rightarrow$

All	24.5091
Model[1]	20.0277
Model[2]	24.9343
Model[3]	28.5653

Our interest lies in the *Model* line. We note the same F-statistic (called *FRatio*) and p-value as before. With this value less than a chosen α-value of 0.05, we reject the null hypothesis that there is no difference between the groups. We can now investigate between which groups the differences are. One of the commonly used *post hoc* tests is the Tukey test. This is available from the list of arguments for the ANOVA function.

Below, we specify this using the PostTests argument and also set the CellMeans to False so as not to view it again:

In[93]:= **ANOVA[anovaTable, PostTests → Tukey, CellMeans → False]**

Out[93]= $\left\{\text{ANOVA} \rightarrow\right.$

	DF	SumOfSq	MeanSq	FRatio	PValue
Model	2	1101.48	550.742	13.9849	5.41634×10^{-6}
Error	87	3426.17	39.3813		
Total	89	4527.65			

,

$\text{PostTests} \rightarrow \{\text{Model} \rightarrow \text{Tukey } \{\{1, 2\}, \{1, 3\}\}\}\Big\}$

We note that there were significant differences between groups A and B and also between groups A and C.

Exercises

10.1 Create a computer variable named **group1** to hold a list object of 100 random values along a normal distribution with a mean of 30 and a standard deviation of 5. Repeat the process for two more list objects with the same mean and standard deviation. Name them **group2** and **group3**. These will be considered the data point values for a single, dependent variable.

10.2 Calculate the mean, standard deviation, and quartiles for each of the three List objects.

10.3 Create a box-and-whisker plot containing three elements, one for each of the three list objects. Be sure to add a label to identify them. Also indicate any potential outliers.

10.4 Use standardization to identify any value in each of the three list objects that are more than three standard deviations away from the mean.

10.5 Use a q-q plot for each of the list objects to make sure that they follow a normal distribution. Does this meet the assumption of normality for the use of parametric tests?

10.6 Use the Shapiro–Wilk test to confirm your visual decision above.

10.7   Calculate the test statistic and *p*-value using the Student *t* test comparing the means of group1 and group2 and express the results in table form.

10.8   Create a list object named **anova** that contains a nested list in the correct form for use as an argument in the ANOVA function. Use all three list objects.

10.9   Calculate the F-statistic and *p*-value for the ANOVA test comparing all three list objects. (Remember to import the ANOVA Package).

More to Explore

For a handy tutorial on the advanced uses of the ANOVA Package, try this (wolfr.am/ANOVA)

There is a great Demonstration on the α-ratio by F. Giraud-Carrier on the Wolfram Demonstrations Project website; check it out (wolfr.am/Visual-ANOVA)

11 | Correlation

In the previous chapter, we compared the mean of data point values for a single variable between groups. The groups were created from the sample space of a categorical variable, i.e. group A and group B for the variable group.

In this chapter, we continue our journey through the exciting world of parametric tests but compare two separate numerical variables to see if there is a relationship between them. To do so, I will introduce concepts of linear regression, which will be covered in more detail in the next chapter, that might help us in understanding correlation.

Relationships

Correlation is all about the relationship between numerical values for two variables. High-school algebra should have made you familiar with a function like $y = 3x$. For every value of x that we plug in to the equation, we get a y value. In that way, y is dependent on x. That's why we use terms such as the independent variable, x, and the dependent variable, y.

If we consider x a continuous, numerical variable that can take any value in the closed domain 0 to 10, which means 0 and 10 are included, we can plot this function. The Plot function, as used in the first example, takes two arguments. The first is the expression on the right-hand side of the equation. The second argument is a list (therefore in curly braces) that explains the closed domain for the x values.

Plot the equation $y = 3x$:

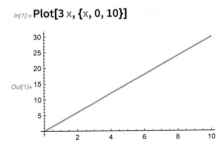

In[1]:= **Plot[3 x, {x, 0, 10}]**

Imagine now that the x values represent a numerical variable such as length. The y values can represent another numerical variable such as width. What we have here then is a model that predicts the value of the width (y) given a value for the length (x). For a simple model such as $y = 3\,x$, we have a perfect correlation between these two variables. As the length increases, the width increases threefold. We can create a function using the Wolfram Language to express this. Note the use of a trailing underscore for the dependent variable and the colon and equal sign. The trailing underscore (_) identifies this as the independent variable and the colon before the equal sign (:=) tells the Wolfram Language not to execute the code but to hang on until it is called (used). This syntax represents $f(x) = y = 3\,x$.

Create a Wolfram Language function called f that takes an argument x and returns the value that is 3 times x:

In[2]:= **f[x_] := 3 x**

We can now pass values for x (length), which will return a value for y (width).

Calculate the width for a height of 4:

In[3]:= **f[4]**

Out[3]= 12

The solution is 12. Carrying on with our example experiment, let's consider a single hypothetical subject. It has a length of 3 and a width of 9. We can plot this point together with our model using the Show function. This function allows for the creation of more than one plot on the same Cartesian grid.

Plot both the line, using the Plot function, and the point, using the ListPlot function:

In[4]:= **Show[Plot[3 x, {x, 0, 10}], ListPlot[{{3, 9}}, PlotStyle → PointSize[Large]]]**

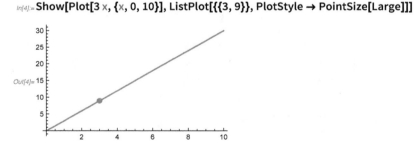

To be sure, this is a very idealized experiment. As mentioned, there is perfect correlation between our two numerical variables. For every single unit increase in length, there is a threefold increase in width. A real experiment will most probably not have these values.

Let's recreate a more realistic example. Next we'll create a nested List object with paired values for length and width for five specimens.

Manually create five subjects, each with data point values for two variables:

In[5]:= **experimentValues = {{1.1, 3.8}, {3.3, 8.5}, {2.1, 7.2}, {6.1, 15.3}, {7.5, 27}}**

Out[5]= {{1.1, 3.8}, {3.3, 8.5}, {2.1, 7.2}, {6.1, 15.3}, {7.5, 27}}

Let's plot those together with our idealized model.

Plot our idealized line and the five subjects:

In[6]:= **Show[Plot[3 x, {x, 0, 10}], ListPlot[experimentValues]]**

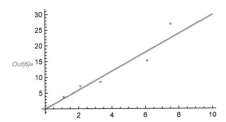

Our model would predict a width of 3.3 given a length of 1.1 as we can see below. In reality, the value was 3.8.

Calculate the width for a height of 1.1:

In[7]:= **f[1.1]**

Out[7]= 3.3

Our model is still very valid. Given a new specimen that was not part of the experiment, we can predict the width if the length is measured. These variables are correlated. This is perhaps a good opportunity to mention the obvious, *correlation does not infer causation*. It does not mean that causation is not present. It is just that showing correlation, as in *the length and width are correlated*, is not proof that the value for the width is somehow caused by the value of the length.

The last thing to consider here is the direction of correlation. The straight line above points to the upper right. This indicates a *positive correlation*. As the values for one variable increase, so do the values for the other. We could also get *negative correlation*, with a decrease in the dependent variable as the independent variable increases. In this case, the line will point to the lower right.

Error

It is obvious to note that our experiment above contained errors. In fact, for the example of a length of 1.1 and real width of 3.8, we can write the following using our model: $3.8 = 3 \times 1.1 + 0.5$ or $y = 3x + \epsilon$. Here, the symbol ϵ is an error value. Indeed, for every true value y_i, we have $y_i = \beta x_i + \epsilon_i$. The subscript i notation is commonly used in statistics. If we have five specimens, we can view i as holding the values 1, 2, 3, 4, 5. Again referring to our example, we note $x_1 = 1.1$ with $y_1 = 3.8$, $x_2 = 3.3$ with $y_2 = 8.5$, and so on. Every pair will have its own error. The first error is $\epsilon_1 = 0.5$, the second error is $\epsilon_2 = -1.4$ (since $3 \times 3.3 = 9.9$ and the true value was 8.5, with $8.5 - 9.9 = -1.4$), and so on. The β in the equation represents the actual relationship in the model (the slope of the line).

As we will see in the next chapter on linear regression, we calculate our linear model (the equation for our straight line) by minimizing this error, and this will give us a value for β.

Covariance

We are well underway in understanding how to create a correlation model given a set of paired values from an experiment.

Next up on our list of requirements is understanding *covariance*. You will recognize the *variance* part of the word. Remember that variance is the square of the average difference between each data point value for a variable and its mean. The square root of the variance is the standard deviation given in equation (1).

$$\sigma^2 = \frac{\sum_{i=1}^{n} (x_i - \bar{x})^2}{n - 1} \tag{1}$$

Here $\bar{x}$ is the mean and n is the number of data point values for a variable. Since we subtract 1 from the sample size, the variance and standard deviation is the *sample* variance and standard deviation. This is opposed to the *population* variance and standard deviation.

Now consider our length and width experiment. If these two variables are indeed correlated, we should see one variable deviate from its mean just as the other would. The difference between a data point value and its mean is called the *deviation* or the *residual*.

If we consider a pair of values for a specimen in our experiment, where each one of the values in the pair belongs to a variable, we might see one below its mean in the same way as the other. This would indicate that we will find a correlation between the two variables.

Multiplying the differences that each pair has with their respective means gives us an equation that represents a correlation between the residuals. This is called covariance, c, and for samples (instead of a population), this is given by equation (2).

$$c = \frac{\sum_{i=1}^{n} (x_i - \bar{x})(y_i - \bar{y})}{n - 1} \tag{2}$$

Let's create two lists of data point values from our example and calculate the covariance using the **Covariance** function in the Wolfram Language.

All the first elements in the pairs:

In[8]:= **length = experimentValues[[All, 1]]**

Out[8]= {1.1, 3.3, 2.1, 6.1, 7.5}

All the second elements in the pairs:

In[9]:= **width = experimentValues[All, 2]**

Out[9]= {3.8, 8.5, 7.2, 15.3, 27}

Calculate the covariance:

In[10]:= **Covariance[length, width]**

Out[10]= 23.686

A positive value indicates positive correlation and a negative value indicates negative correlation. Unfortunately, the magnitude of the covariance does not help us when it comes to the magnitude of the correlation. The actual value, instead, depends on the data point values. If our experiment used micrometers for the unit of the length and width, covariance would be measured in μm^2. If it was measured in millimeters, it would be in mm^2. In order to express the magnitude, we need to *standardize* the covariance.

One useful way of doing this is to express the value in units of standard deviation, i.e. divide by the standard deviation. In the evaluation of a sample, the standardized covariance is known as the correlation coefficient, denoted by the symbol r. It is also known as the *Pearson product-moment correlation coefficient*, or the *Pearson correlation coefficient* for short, and is shown in equation (3).

$$r = \frac{\sum_{i=1}^{n}(x_i - \bar{x})(y_i - \bar{y})}{(n-1)\, s_x\, s_y} \tag{3}$$

Here, s_x and s_y are the standard deviations for the two variables. We can calculate this using the Correlation function in the Wolfram Language.

Calculate the correlation coefficient:

In[11]:= **Correlation[length, width]**

Out[11]= 0.954523

The same can be achieved by calculating the ratio of the covariance (in the numerator) and the product of the standard deviations of the two variables (in the denominator), shown in equation (4).

$$r = \frac{c}{s_x\, s_y} \tag{4}$$

Now try dividing the covariance by the product of the two standard deviations:

In[12]:= $\dfrac{\textbf{Covariance[length, width]}}{\textbf{StandardDeviation[length]} * \textbf{StandardDeviation[width]}}$

Out[12]= 0.954523

The value for r will always fall in the closed domain -1 to $+1$. The former indicates a perfect negative correlation and the latter indicates effective positive correlation.

As some fields in science move away from the ubiquitous use of p-values, we see more and more reports stipulating an effect size. The Pearson correlation coefficient is a perfect example of the measure of effect size. Values between ± 0.1 show very little correlation. Values between 0.1 and 0.3 or -0.1 and -0.3 indicate a small effect. Values between 0.30 and 0.5 or between -0.3 and -0.5 show a medium effect, and values between 0.5 and 1.0 or -0.5 and -1.0 show a large effect. These are simply rules of thumb, though, and you should always view the results in the context of the experiment and the outcomes.

Hypothesis Testing

Having mentioned p-values, though, we can look at the probability of a specific r-value, i.e. testing the hypothesis that the correlation is different from zero, indicating no correlation (the null hypothesis).

The theoretical distribution of the Pearson correlation coefficient, r, is not known. We can convert it to a test statistic by transforming it, though. This is shown in equation (5).

$$z_r = \frac{1}{2} \ln \left(\frac{1+r}{1-r} \right) \tag{5}$$

This z_r has a standard error shown in equation (6).

$$S_z = \frac{1}{\sqrt{n-3}} \tag{6}$$

Using the values for z_r and s_r, we can finally calculate the test statistic, called a z-score (also known as the z-statistic), as shown in equation (7).

$$z = \frac{z_r}{S_z} \tag{7}$$

In the following example, we use the Log function, which calculates the natural logarithm.

Use Log and the correlation that was calculated previously and save it to the computer variable zr:

$$In[13]:= \mathbf{zr} = \frac{1}{2} * \mathbf{Log}[\frac{1 + \mathbf{Correlation[length, width]}}{1 - \mathbf{Correlation[length, width]}}]$$

$Out[13]=$ 1.88035

The standard error is easy to calculate. For our example, which had five pairs of values, we use $n = 5$.

Calculate the standard error and save it in the computer variable sz:

$In[14]:=$ **SZ** $= \dfrac{1}{\sqrt{5-3}}$ **// N**

$Out[14]=$ 0.707107

Now we can calculate the z-score.

Calculate the z-score and saving it in the computer variable z:

$In[15]:=$ **Z** $= \dfrac{zr}{sz}$

$Out[15]=$ 2.65922

Since we are dealing with a sampling distribution, we can use CDF to find the cumulative distribution function. For positive values of z, we calculate $1 - CDF$, and for negative values, we calculate CDF.

Calculate a one-tailed p-value:

$In[16]:=$ **1 − CDF[NormalDistribution[0, 1], z]**

$Out[16]=$ 0.0039161

For a two-tailed hypothesis, we simply multiply this by 2.

Calculate a two-tailed p-value:

$In[17]:=$ **(1 − CDF[NormalDistribution[0, 1], z]) ∗ 2**

$Out[17]=$ 0.00783221

The add-on package Hypothesis Testing, which we used in a previous chapter, has a function called NormalPValue. We pass the calculated z-score to it and can specify that we want a two-tailed p-value.

Import the package:

$In[18]:=$ **Needs["HypothesisTesting`"]**

The default is a one-tailed test:

$In[19]:=$ **NormalPValue[z, TwoSided → True]**

$Out[19]=$ TwoSidedPValue → 0.00783221

We can also construct 95% confidence intervals around the Pearson correlation coefficient. Note that a confidence level of 95% is represented by a standard error of about 1.96. This will be different for different confidence levels. The equation is shown in (8).

$$z_r \pm (1.96 \times S_z) \tag{8}$$

Let's calculate the lower and the upper bounds for a 95% confidence level.

The lower limit of the 95% confidence interval:

In[20]:= **lowerBoundzr = zr − (1.96 ∗ sz)**

Out[20]= 0.494422

The upper limit of the 95% confidence interval:

In[21]:= **upperBoundzr = zr + (1.96 ∗ sz)**

Out[21]= 3.26628

These values can be converted back to r-values as shown in equation (9).

$$r = \frac{e^{(2 \times z_r)} - 1}{e^{(2 \times z_r)} + 1} \tag{9}$$

Here the z_r-values refer to the lower and upper bound values.

Lower r-value:

In[22]:= **rLower = $\dfrac{\text{Exp}[2 \ast \text{lowerBoundzr}] - 1}{\text{Exp}[2 \ast \text{lowerBoundzr}] + 1}$**

Out[22]= 0.457719

Upper r-value:

In[23]:= **rUpper = $\dfrac{\text{Exp}[2 \ast \text{upperBoundzr}] - 1}{\text{Exp}[2 \ast \text{upperBoundzr}] + 1}$**

Out[23]= 0.997094

We can now finally conclude that there is a significant correlation between length and width with a Pearson correlation coefficient, r, of 0.96 (a 95% confidence interval from 0.46 to 1), with a p-value of less than 0.01.

Comparing Correlation Coefficients

It may also be warranted to compare two correlation coefficients. This need arises when the data point values for the numerical variables can be split by another categorical variable. In the next example, we create paired data point values for two species.

Create a theoretical (population) distribution with a mean of 20 and a standard deviation of 5:

In[24]:= **populationDistribution = NormalDistribution[20, 5];**

In the next code cell, we create two sets of 30 paired values taken at random from the population distribution. Each value in a pair represents one of two numerical variables for which we want to find a correlation. We will use the computer variable names speciesA and speciesB.

Create two groups, each with 30 pairs of values taken from the population distribution:

In[25]:= **SeedRandom[123]**
speciesA = RandomVariate[populationDistribution, {30, 2}];
speciesB = RandomVariate[populationDistribution, {30, 2}];

Now we use the ListPlot function to plot the data point value pairs for the two groups. In this case, you will note the use of the Labeled function as one of the arguments. It, in turn, allows us to pass two arguments. The first is the list of paired values and the second is a string name to label the values. Note also that the two sets that are to be plotted are stipulated as a List object.

Show both sets of pairs and label them at the same time using Labeled:

In[28]:= **ListPlot[{Labeled[speciesA, "A"], Labeled[speciesB, "B"]}]**

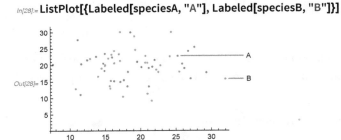

To compare the correlation coefficients, we need to extract each group of data point values from the speciesA and speciesB nested List objects. We can achieve this using addressing. Since each set contains two variables, we will use the computer variables speciesAVar1, speciesAVar2, speciesBVar1, and speciesBVar2 for descriptive purposes to help us later when we review the code or give it to someone else to view.

Extract the first element of each pair in speciesA (nested List object):

In[29]:= **speciesAVar1 = speciesA⟦All, 1⟧;**

Extract the second element of each pair in speciesA:

In[30]:= **speciesAVar2 = speciesA⟦All, 2⟧;**

Extract the first element of each pair in speciesB:

In[31]:= **speciesBVar1 = speciesB⟦All, 1⟧;**

Extract the second element of each pair in speciesB:

In[32]:= **speciesBVar2 = speciesB⟦All, 2⟧;**

Next up, we calculate the correlation coefficient for the speciesA group and the speciesB group using the separated List objects. We will use rA and rB for the two correlation coefficients.

Calculate the correlation coefficient for the speciesA group and save it as variable rA:

In[33]:= **rA = Correlation[speciesAVar1, speciesAVar2]**

Out[33]= 0.043219

Calculate the correlation coefficient for the speciesB group and save it as variable rB:

In[34]:= **rB = Correlation[speciesBVar1, speciesBVar2]**

Out[34]= 0.0272994

We need to calculate a z-score for the difference between these two correlation coefficients. The equation for this, δ_z, is shown in equation (10).

$$\delta z = \frac{r_1 - r_2}{\sqrt{\frac{1}{n_1 - 3} + \frac{1}{n_2 - 3}}} \tag{10}$$

Here, r_1 and r_2 are the two correlation coefficients that we calculated previously. The n_1 and n_2 variables are the sample sizes. As always, we can calculate the sample size using the Length function.

Calculate δ_z and save it in the computer variable dz:

In[35]:= **dz =** $\dfrac{\text{rA} - \text{rB}}{\sqrt{\dfrac{1}{\text{Length[speciesAVar1]} - 3} + \dfrac{1}{\text{Length[speciesBVar1]} - 3}}}$

Out[35]= 0.0584922

Once again, depending on whether the value is negative or positive, we use 1 – CDF or CDF to calculate a p-value and multiply it by 2 for a two-tailed null hypothesis.

Calculate the p-value for δ_z:

In[36]:= **(1 – CDF[NormalDistribution[0, 1], dz]) * 2**

Out[36]= 0.953357

For a chosen α-value of 0.05, we cannot reject the null hypothesis that there is no difference between the correlation coefficients. There is no difference in the correlation between the two numerical variables for the two species.

That's it for correlations and their comparisons. Now you can create your own List objects of numerical variables and test if there are correlations between them. One standard way to do so is to use linear regression, which we will look at in depth next.

Exercises

11.1 Create a List object holding 30 data point values for a variable called var1. Take the values from a normal distribution with a mean of 100 and a standard deviation of 10.

11.2 Create a List object holding 30 data point values for a variable called var2. To do this, use simple elementwise addition of List objects and add a random value with a mean of 5 and a standard deviation of 2 to each of the 30 elements in var1.

11.3 Using the Table function, create a nested List object of each of the 30 data point values in the two variables, var1 and var2, above. Name it var12. The result should be a nested List object in the form {{101.4, 102.2}, {104.8, 108, 4}, …, {99, 9, 105.2}}.

11.4 Create a scatter plot of var12 using the ListPlot function.

11.5 Using the Correlation function, calculate the correlation coefficient for var1 and var2. Save the coefficient as the computer variable r.

11.6 Using the computer variables zr, zs, and z, calculate the z-score as used in equations (5), (6), and (7) in this chapter.

11.7 Import the Hypothesis Testing Package and calculate the two-tailed p-value for the correlation coefficient.

11.8 Using equations (8) and (9), calculate the lower and upper bounds of the correlation coefficient for a confidence level of 95%.

Tech Notes

- _ or Blank is a pattern object that can stand for any Wolfram Language expression.

- lhs := rhs (left-hand side and right-hand side) assigns rhs to be the delayed value of lhs. rhs is maintained in an unevaluated form. When lhs appears, it is replaced by rhs, evaluated afresh each time.

More to Explore

Check out this tutorial on convolutions and correlations (wolfr.am/ConvolutionsCorrelations)

This Demonstration by I. McLeod provides a bird's-eye view of the visualization of correlations (wolfr.am/VisualizingCorrelations)

12 | Linear Regression

In this chapter, we will build on our understanding of model creation that was alluded to at the start of the previous chapter. We are still considering how one variable, the *independent variable*, affects another variable, the *dependent variable*.

Because randomness in the data will almost never give us a perfect prediction, our modeling methods will always hold some error. This error is the difference between the predicted dependent variable data point value and the real data point value, given a specific independent data point value.

The model from which we predict the value of the dependent variable is shown here.

$$y_i = b_0 + b_1 X_i + \varepsilon_i \tag{1}$$

If we forget the error term ε_i for a moment, equation (1) should be familiar from high-school algebra, where we looked at $y = c + mx$. This is an equation for a straight line, with m being the slope of the line and c being the y axis intercept where $x = 0$.

Let's plot such a line for $m = \frac{1}{2}$ and $c = 2$. The equation becomes $y = 2 + \frac{1}{2} x$. At $x = 0$, we have $y = 2$ and therefore the point $(0, 2)$. Because we wish to make two plots on the same coordinate plane, we will use the Show function. The straight line can be created using the Plot function. The y intercept point can be created using the ListPlot function.

Note the double curly braces in the ListPlot function:

In[1]:= Show[Plot[$\frac{1}{2}$x+2, {x, −1, 5}], ListPlot[{{0, 2}}, PlotMarkers → Red]]

Note the slope of $\frac{1}{2}$. This is the rise over run, i.e. we rise one unit on the y axis for every two units we move on the x axis. When $x = 0$, we see that $y = 2$, the y intercept (red square). All we have to do to this conceptual model is add the error term ε_i for every real y value.

Now if we replace c with b_0 and m with b_1, we have the two *regression coefficients* needed for all single independent variable models.

Note that we needn't stick to a single independent variable. Moving up to 3D space, we can calculate a dependent variable by using two independent variables. Going up to 4D in our imagination, we can use three independent variables and so on. The equation for two independent variables is shown in equation (2).

$$y_i = b_0 + b_1 X_i + b_2 X_2 + \varepsilon_i \tag{2}$$

Calculating the Regression Coefficients

It is time to bring back the error term. Our aim (for a single independent variable) is to create an equation that best fits the data. Real-world data never fits a straight line because there is always some noise or variability to contend with.

We can sum up our problem in the next plot. It shows value pairs for the independent and dependent variables and a few straight lines. The straight lines represent our linear model that predicts a dependent variable data point value given an independent data point value. But how do we choose between these models?

Below we plot our data point values. The x coordinate of each point comes from the independent variable and the y coordinate comes from the dependent variable for each corresponding subject. To *guess* the correct lines, we will use three sets of regression coefficients (slope, or b_1, and intercept, or b_0). The three equations are shown in (3).

$$\begin{aligned} y &= -0.5 + x \\ y &= 1 + x \\ y &= -0.3 + 1.2\,x \end{aligned} \tag{3}$$

Create a plot with the data point values and three possible models using the Show function with ListPlot for the markers and Plot for the models:

```
In[2]:= Show[ListPlot[{{1, 1}, {2, 1.5}, {3, 3.1}, {4, 4.5}, {5, 5}}, PlotMarkers → Red],
         Plot[{x−0.5, x+1, 1.2 x−0.3}, {x, −1, 10}]]
```

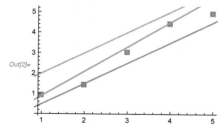

Out[2]=

Given the data point values for the two variables, there is a mathematical way of calculating the best regression coefficients (b_0 and b_1).

We start by adding the squares of the errors, which, as we remember, are the differences between the predicted value and the actual value, also called the *residuals*. This is called the *sum of squared residuals* or *residual sum of squares*. Note that we square the errors so that we have positive values because some of the real values will be above and some below the predicted line and these will cancel if we simply add them.

So what we aim to do is to look for regression coefficients based on trying to minimize this sum of squared residuals. The smaller this value, the better the final line models our data.

There are beautiful equations to do this, either using vector calculus or gradient descent. These are quite difficult to do. To calculate the regression coefficients using the Wolfram Language could not be any easier, though.

First, let's create two variables, an independent variable and a dependent variable. Below is a nested List object that contains the values for each of these variables as pairs, one for each of the 10 subjects in a simulated experiment. We will add this object to a computer variable called **data**. We'll also create a scatter plot, which we might intuitively interpret as some correlation existing between the variables.

Create 10 pairs of values and save them in the computer variable **data**:

```
In[3]:= data = {{0, 1}, {0.5, 1.8}, {1, 2}, {1.3, 2.9},
        {2.1, 3}, {2.5, 4.9}, {2.9, 6.1}, {3.7, 8.8}, {4, 8.7}, {4.9, 9.9}};
```

Create a plot of the data points:

```
In[4]:= ListPlot[data, PlotStyle → {PointSize[Medium], Red}]
```

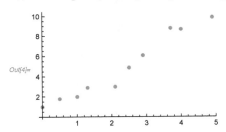

Now we use the LinearModelFit function and pass the data point values. Note the full list of arguments that contain two *x*'s. Let's call the computer variable linearModel.

Create a single independent variable linear model:

```
In[5]:= linearModel = LinearModelFit[data, x, x]
```

Out[5]= FittedModel[0.349388 + 1.99153 x]

The model that we created has many properties that we can examine.

List all the properties for our model:

In[6]:= **linearModel["Properties"]**

Out[6]= {AdjustedRSquared, AIC, AICc, ANOVATable, ANOVATableDegreesOfFreedom, ANOVATableEntries, ANOVATableFStatistics, ANOVATableMeanSquares, ANOVATablePValues, ANOVATableSumsOfSquares, BasisFunctions, BetaDifferences, BestFit, BestFitParameters, BIC, CatcherMatrix, CoefficientOfVariation, CookDistances, CorrelationMatrix, CovarianceMatrix, CovarianceRatios, Data, DesignMatrix, DurbinWatsonD, EigenstructureTable, EigenstructureTableEigenvalues, EigenstructureTableEntries, EigenstructureTableIndexes, EigenstructureTablePartitions, EstimatedVariance, FitDifferences, FitResiduals, Function, FVarianceRatios, HatDiagonal, MeanPredictionBands, MeanPredictionConfidenceIntervals, MeanPredictionConfidenceIntervalTable, MeanPredictionConfidenceIntervalTableEntries, MeanPredictionErrors, ParameterConfidenceIntervals, ParameterConfidenceIntervalTable, ParameterConfidenceIntervalTableEntries, ParameterConfidenceRegion, ParameterErrors, ParameterPValues, ParameterTable, ParameterTableEntries, ParameterTStatistics, PartialSumOfSquares, PredictedResponse, Properties, Response, RSquared, SequentialSumOfSquares, SingleDeletionVariances, SinglePredictionBands, SinglePredictionConfidenceIntervals, SinglePredictionConfidenceIntervalTable, SinglePredictionConfidenceIntervalTableEntries, SinglePredictionErrors, StandardizedResiduals, StudentizedResiduals, VarianceInflationFactors}

One of these properties is "**ParameterTable**". The estimate in the first row is our y intercept and the estimate in the second row is the slope. As you can see, there is a lot more interesting information in this table.

Let's see where the property "**ParameterTable**" gets us:

In[7]:= **linearModel["ParameterTable"]**

	Estimate	Standard Error	t-Statistic	P-Value
Out[7]= 1	0.349388	0.434381	0.804335	0.444446
x	1.99153	0.157868	12.6152	1.46337×10^{-6}

Concentrating on the two estimates, we now have a value for each of our two required regression coefficients. We now have a y intercept, b_0, and a slope, b_1 (the estimate values for 1 and x above), so we can plot this straight line model.

Plot our data point values and linear model:

In[8]:= **Show[ListPlot[data, PlotStyle → {PointSize[Medium], Red}], Plot[linearModel[x], {x, 0, 5}]]**

Out[8]=

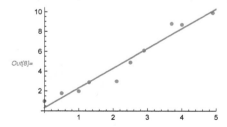

If we draw an imaginary line straight up or down from a given x axis (independent variable) value on our model line, we get a predicted y axis (dependent variable) value. Drawing two imaginary lines, one from the actual marker and one from the point on the line to the left (the y axis), produces two points on the axis. The difference between these is our residual or error, that is, the difference between the true and the predicted values, or the ε_i in equation (1).

We can use the "FitResiduals" property to show the error for each predicted versus actual dependent variable data point value and then plot them.

List the residuals, the actual value minus the predicted value:

In[9]:= **linearModel["FitResiduals"]**

Out[9]= {0.650612, 0.454846, −0.340921, −0.0383815,
    −1.53161, −0.428222, −0.0248356, 1.08194, 0.384477, −0.207903}

The plot of the residuals shows their magnitude and whether they were lower or higher than the actual values.

Plot the residuals:

In[10]:= **ListPlot[linearModel["FitResiduals"], Filling → Axis]**

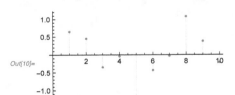

Out[10]=

Calculating How Well the Model Fits the Data

Now that we have a model, we need to know how good it is. We cheated a bit with our model above. The data point values for the variables were chosen to show a very good correlation. Things can look a lot worse. Next is an example of some random values. In keeping with the explanation, we will call the List object badData. Even such data can have a model fitted to it though.

Create 20 pairs of integer values in the domain 1 through 10:

In[11]:= **badData = {{2, 2}, {3, 9}, {2, 3}, {10, 8}, {5, 9}, {7, 3}, {10, 5}, {7, 1}, {9, 3}, {8, 2},**
    {5, 4}, {7, 1}, {7, 1}, {10, 7}, {2, 9}, {10, 2}, {7, 1}, {7, 7}, {2, 2}, {10, 8}};

A scatter plot for this looks a bit chaotic.

Create a plot of the data point pairs:

In[12]:= ListPlot[badData, PlotStyle → {PointSize[Medium], Red}]

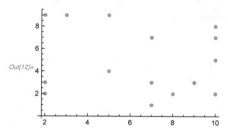

Let's create a linear model and call it badLinearModel, which we will plot.

Create a linear model:

In[13]:= badLinearModel = LinearModelFit[badData, x, x]

Out[13]= FittedModel[4.36923 − 0.00295858 x]

Plot the model:

In[14]:= Show[ListPlot[badData], Plot[badLinearModel[x], {x, 0, 10}]]

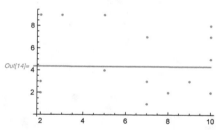

The residual plot shows large errors.

Plot the residuals:

In[15]:= ListPlot[badLinearModel["FitResiduals"], Filling → Axis]

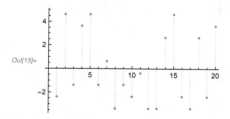

One way to assess how good our model is at predicting the dependent variable is by calculating the R^2 value, called the *coefficient of determination*. This is a property in the model object itself. Look below at the difference between the badLinearModel and the linearModel examples.

R^2 for the bad model:

In[16]:= **badLinearModel["RSquared"]**

Out[16]= 8.28502×10^{-6}

R^2 for the good model:

In[17]:= **linearModel["RSquared"]**

Out[17]= 0.952137

An R^2 value closer to 1 relates to a much better predictive model while a value closer to 0 is, in essence, just random.

How is this R^2 value calculated? It is basically a comparison of our model with a model based on the mean of the dependent variable. Let's look at our first model's data point value pairs for its two variables. Remember that the first value in the pair was the independent variable and the second was the dependent variable. Represented as a Wolfram Language nested List object, these 10 pairs represent the data point values for two variables for 10 subjects in an experiment, as we discussed previously.

Our first job is to isolate the dependent variable as a list using index addressing. We'll call the computer variable dataOutcome.

Index all of the second elements:

In[18]:= **dataOutcome = data[[All, 2]]**

Out[18]= {1, 1.8, 2, 2.9, 3, 4.9, 6.1, 8.8, 8.7, 9.9}

Now we calculate the mean of this new List object and attach it to the computer variable meanOutcome.

Find the mean of the dependent variable:

In[19]:= **meanOutcome = Mean[dataOutcome]**

Out[19]= 4.91

Now we have to calculate the *total sum of squares*, which is similar to calculating residuals, but instead of using the predicted values, we subtract the mean from every observed value and square each of these differences. Finally, we sum all of the squared terms. We use the Table function and run through each of the elements in dataOutcome. We subtract the mean from each value and square the difference. Notice the use of the Length function to ensure that we iterate through all the elements. All of these are wrapped as arguments in the Total function, which sums the elements in the List object. We'll call the List object totalSumOfSquares.

Calculate the total sum of squares:

In[20]:= **totalSumOfSquares =**
 Total[Table[(dataOutcome[[n]] − meanOutcome)^2, {n, 1, Length[dataOutcome]}]]

Out[20]= 96.929

While using the Table function as an iterator works well for a relatively small number of data point values, it is much more efficient to use *vectorized* functions, especially with large datasets. Next we simply subtract the two List objects from each other. This will be done elementwise. The results of these elementwise subtractions will be squared.

The Total function will finally add all of these squared elements:

In[21]:= **totalSumOfSquares = Total[(dataOutcome − meanOutcome)^2]**

Out[21]= 96.929

Remember the "FitResidual" property of our model? It was an easy way to get a List object of all the errors (difference between predicted and observed values of the dependent variable). We attach it to the computer variable residuals. Note that we could also construct Wolfram Language code to get this List object as with the totalSumOfSquares.

Save the model residuals:

In[22]:= **residuals = linearModel["FitResiduals"]**

Out[22]= {0.650612, 0.454846, −0.340921, −0.0383815,
 −1.53161, −0.428222, −0.0248356, 1.08194, 0.384477, −0.207903}

Now we need to square each of these values and add all of them. We'll call the result residualSumOfSquares. In the next example, we use a vectorized function instead of iterating over all of the elements using the Table function.

Calculate the residual sum of squares for the model:

In[23]:= **residualSumOfSquares = Total[residuals^2]**

Out[23]= 4.63933

The R^2 value is the difference between the total sum of squares and the residual sum of squares divided by the total sum of squares. It is a ratio comparing our model to a very basic model that uses the mean of the dependent variable as the sole predictor value for all the subjects.

Calculate the R^2 value:

In[24]:= $\dfrac{\textbf{totalSumOfSquares} - \textbf{residualSumOfSquares}}{\textbf{totalSumOfSquares}}$

Out[24]= 0.952137

What is the meaning of the R^2 value? Well, it represents the variance in the dependent variable explained by the model (difference between the total sum of squares and the residual sum of squares) relative to how much variance there was to begin with (the total sum of squares).

We can express it as a percentage and indeed view it as the percentage of the variation in the outcome that the model explains.

The p-value for the coefficient of determination can also be calculated. To do this, we first need Fisher's ratio, usually denoted as the F-ratio. This ratio is shown in equation (6).

$$F = \frac{(n - k - 1)\,R^2}{k(1 - R^2)} \tag{4}$$

Here, n is the total number of subjects in the study and k is the number of independent (predictor) variables.

Use the previously calculated R^2 value:

In[25]:= $\textbf{F} = \dfrac{\textbf{(10 − 1 − 1) * 0.952137}}{\textbf{1 * (1 − 0.952137)}}$

Out[25]= 159.144

The p-value for the F-statistic can be calculated using the CDF function. Here we use FRatioDistribution. It takes two arguments, both indicating degrees of freedom. The first indicates the total number of independent variables (add 1 for the intercept), and the second is the total number of subjects minus the number of independent variables (add 1 for the intercept).

We use 1 − CDF in calculating the p-value and multiply by 2 for a two-tailed hypothesis.

Calculate the p-value:

In[26]:= **(1 − CDF[FRatioDistribution[2, 8], F]) * 2**

Out[26]= 7.22751×10^{-7}

We have found a significant p-value, as expected.

In the next plot, we note just how *extreme* this particular F-statistic is. Remember that the *p*-value is represented by the area under the curve to the right of the F-statistic (marked by the vertical line).

Use PlotStyle to note the F-statistic:

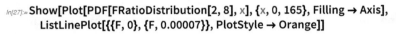
In[27]:= **Show[Plot[PDF[FRatioDistribution[2, 8], x], {x, 0, 165}, Filling → Axis],**
ListLinePlot[{{F, 0}, {F, 0.00007}}, PlotStyle → Orange]]

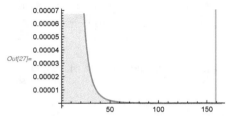

Out[27]=

Assessing Bias

As part of inferential statistics, the goal of linear regression is to generalize to the wider population from which a research sample was taken and that constitutes the data we have to work with. We might have an excellent fit for our model, but if bias was introduced when selecting the sample, our hard work in generating a model means very little.

In a common form of bias, our model is influenced by a small number of data point values. These influential cases are called *outliers*. Below we create two experiments that differ only in a single dependent data point value.

Our good example data:

In[28]:= **data**

Out[28]= {{0, 1}, {0.5, 1.8}, {1, 2}, {1.3, 2.9}, {2.1, 3}, {2.5, 4.9}, {2.9, 6.1}, {3.7, 8.8}, {4, 8.7}, {4.9, 9.9}}

Let's only change the last dependent variable data point value from 9.9 to 1.2. We'll call this List object dataOutlier.

Create a single outlier:

In[29]:= **dataOutlier = {{0, 1}, {0.5, 1.8}, {1, 2}, {1.3, 2.9},**
{2.1, 3}, {2.5, 4.9}, {2.9, 6.1}, {3.7, 8.8}, {4, 8.7}, {4.9, 1.2}};

We can create another linear model, linearModelOutlier.

Create a new linear model:

In[30]:= **linearModelOutlier = LinearModelFit[dataOutlier, x, x]**

Out[30]= FittedModel[1.71408 + 1.01569 x]

Now have a look at the difference between the two models (the model with the outlier is in red).

Plot a model for each of the datasets:

In[31]:= **Show[ListPlot[{data, dataOutlier}, PlotStyle → PointSize[Medium]],**
Plot[linearModel[x], {x, 0, 5}], Plot[linearModelOutlier[x], {x, 0, 5},
PlotStyle → {Thick, Red}], ListPlot[{{4.9, 1.2}}, PlotMarkers → Red]]

Out[31]=

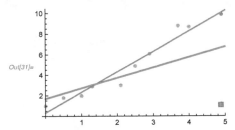

Note that the residual for an outlier will be bigger than the rest.

Calculate the residuals:

In[32]:= **linearModelOutlier["FitResiduals"]**

Out[32]= {−0.714079, −0.421922, −0.729765, −0.134471,
−0.84702, 0.646706, 1.44043, 3.32788, 2.92318, −5.49094}

While the observed value was 1.2, the predicted (calculated) data point value is 6.69094. We can calculate this by simply passing the independent variable data point value to the model object.

Calculate the predicted dependent value:

In[33]:= **linearModelOutlier[4.9]**

Out[33]= **6.69094**

The difference between the actual and predicted value is as we see in the last item of the list above.

Calculate the difference manually:

In[34]:= **1.2 − 6.69094**

Out[34]= **−5.49094**

We need a way of deciding if this is out of keeping with the rest of the residuals. Unfortunately, the residuals are measured in the same units as the variables. We need to standardize them, which means centralizing and expressing them in units of standard deviation. This is simply a property of our model object called "StandardizedResiduals".

Calculate the standardized residuals:

In[35]:= **linearModelOutlier["StandardizedResiduals"]**

Out[35]= {−0.33395, −0.185625, −0.30797, −0.0557677,
−0.343254, 0.262127, 0.588481, 1.41636, 1.27602, −2.70665}

Plotting these clearly shows the outlier.

Plot the standardized residuals:

In[36]:= **ListPlot[linearModelOutlier["StandardizedResiduals"], Filling → Axis, PlotRange → All]**

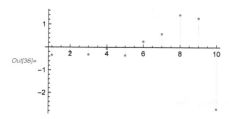

Out[36]=

The standardized residuals follow the standard normal distribution with a mean of 0 and a standard deviation of 1. With the standardized residual being −2.70665 (below zero), we can calculate the probability of such a low value using CDF. If the value was greater than 0, we would use 1 − CDF. We pass as arguments the distribution we require and the value.

Omit arguments for the NormalDistribution function to indicate standard normal distribution:

In[37]:= **CDF[NormalDistribution[], −2.70665]**

Out[37]= 0.00339829

This is a low probability indeed. In general, we would call our model a bad generalization under the following circumstances:

1. A standardized residual less than −3.29 or more than 3.29
2. If more than 1% of the cases have a standardized residual of less than −2.58 or more than 2.58
3. If more than 5% of the cases have a standardized residuals of less than −1.96 or more than 1.96

These values are based on the PDF of the standard normal distribution:

In[38]:= **Plot[PDF[NormalDistribution[], x], {x, −5, 5}, Filling → Axis]**

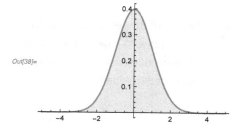

Out[38]=

Let's consider the 95% quantile values. This would be the values at 0.025 and at 0.975.

The quantile values are saved as lL and uL for use in the plot:

In[39]:= **{lL, uL} = Quantile[NormalDistribution[], {0.025, 0.975}]**

Out[39]= **{−1.95996, 1.95996}**

In the next plot, we note these quantile values as vertical lines. The area under the curve to the left of the blue line plus the area to the right of the orange line together represents 0.05 (5%) of the total area under the curve.

Show combines the Plot with the List, showing the specific area desired:

In[40]:= **Show[Plot[PDF[NormalDistribution[], x], {x, −5, 5}, Filling → Axis],**
ListLinePlot[{{{lL, 0}, {lL, 0.4}}, {{uL, 0}, {uL, 0.4}}}]]

Out[40]=

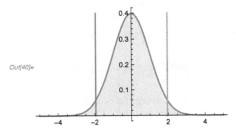

The quantile values for 99% are shown below, followed by the values for 99.95%:

In[41]:= **Quantile[NormalDistribution[], {0.005, 0.997}]**

Out[41]= **{−2.57583, 2.74778}**

In[42]:= **Quantile[NormalDistribution[], {0.0005, 0.9995}]**

Out[42]= **{−3.29053, 3.29053}**

Linear regression can be a powerful predictive tool and forms the basis of many machine learning algorithms.

Exercises

You can find the notebooks for this textbook at wolfr.am/klopper. All relevant .csv files are stored in the downloadable .zip file. If you are using a fresh notebook, make sure to have the .csv stored in the same folder.

12.1   Import the *LinearRegression.csv* file using the SemanticImport function. Save the imported dataset as the computer variable **data**. (Hint: if the import fails, use the Delimiters −> "," argument.)

12.2   View the first five rows of data.

12.3   Create a scatter plot of the input versus the output variable.

12.4   Extract both variables as lists and save them individually as computer variables named inputVariable and outputVariable.

12.5   Use Table or Transpose to create a nested list of pairs from the two List objects above. Name the object pairedVariables.

12.6 Create a linear model object named linearModel from pairedVariables.

12.7 Show the parameter table for linearModel.

12.8 Use Show to plot both the paired data point values (pairedVariables) and the fitted line (linearModel).

12.9 Create a smooth histogram of the residuals linearModel.

12.10 Calculate the R^2 value for linearModel using its properties.

Tech Notes

- Delimiter is an option for various functions that specifies what delimiters to use or look for.
  reference.wolfram.com/language/ref/Delimiter.html

More to Explore

The Wolfram|Alpha page on regression analysis provides some fun demonstrations for students (wolfr.am/regression-analysis)

For a visual proof of Lagrange's sum of squares, try this Wolfram Demonstration by M. Schreiber (wolfr.am/SumOfSquares)

For the advanced, read about using artificial neural nets for statistical discovery and clinical trial data in the open access journal *Complex Systems* (wolfr.am/v03_i03_a05)

In Chapter 8, we came across the χ^2 distribution. It is dependent on the concept of degrees of freedom. This distribution is well suited to see if the counts of a set of data point values for a variable follows a specific distribution, using it as a *goodness-of-fit* test. In its more common form, we look at the independence of categorical groups and perform the well-known χ^2 test of independence.

Just as a reminder, let's plot the χ^2 distribution for 2, 6, and 20 degrees of freedom.

Plot three χ^2 distributions with varying degrees of freedom:

```
In[1]:= Plot[Table[PDF[ChiSquareDistribution[δ], x], {δ, {2, 6, 20}}] // Evaluate,
        {x, 0, 50}, Filling → Axis, PlotRange → All, PlotLabel → "χ² Distributions",
        AxesLabel → {"", "Probability"}, PlotLegends → {"2", "6", "20"}]
```

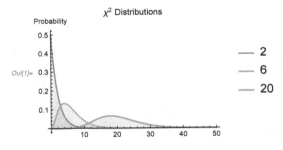

χ^2 Test of Goodness of Fit

With this test, we want to calculate whether a set of data point values for a variable follows a certain predicted proportion of counts. When we compared two means using parametric tests, we made use of the normal or t distributions. When we consider categorial variables, we make use of the χ^2 distribution.

As an example, let's consider a survey in which participants could choose one of five answers to a statement. Even though these are numbers, they represent an ordinal categorical variable. Our experiment will have 100 participants.

Create a list of 100 data point values from the sample space 1 through 5:

```
In[2]:= SeedRandom[123];
        data = RandomInteger[{1, 5}, 100]
```

```
Out[3]= {4, 2, 3, 1, 1, 3, 4, 2, 2, 5, 1, 2, 5, 4, 3, 3, 5, 5, 3, 5, 2, 2, 5, 3, 1, 2, 2, 1, 5, 1, 5, 4, 2, 2,
         3, 5, 2, 1, 4, 3, 4, 4, 2, 4, 2, 2, 4, 2, 3, 1, 2, 2, 3, 3, 5, 1, 4, 3, 2, 5, 3, 1, 2, 1, 4, 5, 4,
         1, 3, 5, 5, 4, 1, 4, 3, 3, 3, 2, 5, 3, 4, 2, 5, 5, 5, 3, 1, 2, 1, 1, 2, 2, 1, 4, 3, 2, 1, 4, 5, 5}
```

We can check on the proportion of choices using the Tally function.

Count the occurrence of each of the unique data point values:

```
In[4]:= SortBy[Tally[data], Greater]
```

```
Out[4]= {{1, 18}, {2, 25}, {3, 20}, {4, 17}, {5, 20}}
```

We note that choice 1 occurred 18 times, 2 occurred 25 times, 3 occurred 20 times, 4 occurred 17 times, and 5 occurred 20 times. We can save the counts as a List object and calculate the total number of data point values using the Length function. We can then store these in appropriately named computer variables for later use.

Store the counts and the sample size:

```
In[5]:= counts = {18, 25, 20, 17, 20}
```

```
Out[5]= {18, 25, 20, 17, 20}
```

```
In[6]:= n = Length[data]
```

```
Out[6]= 100
```

Imagine, though, that we expected the chosen answers to appear with equal proportion. That means that we expected 20% of people to have chosen 1, 20% to have chosen 2, and so on. The question is: How does our observed count distribution differ from this expected count distribution?

The χ^2 tests are based on equation (1). These tests are a form of ratio between what the observed counts in our experiments are and what we expected the counts to be.

$$\chi^2 = \sum \frac{(\text{observed} - \text{expected})^2}{\text{expected}} \tag{1}$$

In the specific case of goodness of fit, we have equation (2).

$$\chi^2 = \sum_{i=1}^{n} \frac{(y_i - \text{np}_i)^2}{\text{np}_i} \tag{2}$$

Here, n is the sample size; every y_i is a count of a specific, unique sample space value as observed; and p_i is the expected proportion for each specific, unique sample space data point value, so in our example, we would have $n = 100$, $y_1 = 18$, $y_2 = 25$, $y_3 = 20$,

$y_4 = 17$, $y_5 = 20$, and $p_1 = p_2 = p_3 = p_4 = p_5 = 0.2$. Note that all the probabilities sum to 1.0, as they should. First, let's create a List object to hold the probabilities.

Create a List object of the probabilities, using Table to repeat the values:

In[7]:= **p = Table[0.2, {5}]**

Out[7]= {0.2, 0.2, 0.2, 0.2, 0.2}

Next, we simply plug these values into the equation and save it in the computer variable chiSquare.

Store the values in chiSquare:

In[8]:= **chiSquare = Total[$\dfrac{(\text{counts} - n \times p)^2}{n \times p}$]**

Out[8]= 1.9

We can calculate a *p*-value for $\chi^2 = 1.9$ for a specific degree of freedom. In this case, the latter is 4. We get this from subtracting the number of the variable, 1 in this case, from the number of unique sample space elements, which is 5.

Since we need the area under the curve from our χ^2 value out toward positive infinity, we use the CDF function subtracted from 1.

Calculate a *p*-value:

In[9]:= **1 – CDF[ChiSquareDistribution[4], chiSquare]**

Out[9]= 0.754145

For a visual representation, a plot of the χ^2 distribution with 4 degrees of freedom, together with our specific χ^2 value drawn as a vertical line at 1.9, shows the large area under the curve toward positive infinity, i.e. the large *p*-value.

Plot the appropriate curve with the calculated χ^2 value:

In[10]:= **Plot[PDF[ChiSquareDistribution[4], x], {x, 0, 20},**
    PlotLabel → "χ^2 Distribution with 4 Degrees of Freedom",
    Filling → Axis, Epilog → Line[{{chiSquare, 0}, {chiSquare, 0.2}}]]

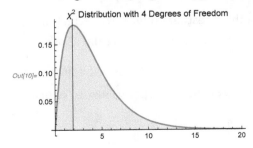

With some care, we can also do this test using the DistrubutionFitTest function. This will only work when we have a discrete set of observed values and a discrete uniform distribution, i.e. the expected proportions are equal. It is intended as a function with broader applicability to testing an observed set of data point values against a known distribution. It is commonly used in that setting and not for a goodness-of-fit test as we intend here.

If used in our simple example case, the first argument is our data. The second argument is the distribution that we expected. In this case, it was the discrete normal distribution of the values 1 through 5, intended as an ordinal categorical data type. Using the "TestDataTable" argument will give us the appropriate test (in this case, it will be the χ^2 test of goodness of fit, called Pearson χ^2), with its statistic and p-value.

Use the DistributionFitTest function and specify a suspected DiscreteUniformDistribution:

In[11]:= **DistributionFitTest[data, DiscreteUniformDistribution[{1, 5}], "TestDataTable"]**

Out[11]=

	Statistic	P-Value
Pearson χ^2	1.9	0.754145

For a chosen α-value of 0.05, we note that we cannot reject the null hypothesis. The "TestConclusion" property will state this explicitly.

Use the "TestConclusion" property:

In[12]:= **DistributionFitTest[data, DiscreteUniformDistribution[{1, 5}], "TestConclusion"]**

Out[12]= The null hypothesis that
the data is distributed according to the DiscreteUniformDistribution[{1, 5}]
is not rejected at the 5 percent level based on the Pearson χ^2 test.

It is easy to change the chosen α-value using the SignificanceLevel argument. Next, we set it to 0.01. Notice the change in the wording of the conclusion to reflect our choice of 1%.

Set α to 0.01:

In[13]:= **DistributionFitTest[data, DiscreteUniformDistribution[{1, 5}],**
    "TestConclusion", SignificanceLevel → 0.01]

Out[13]= The null hypothesis that
the data is distributed according to the DiscreteUniformDistribution[{1, 5}]
is not rejected at the 1. percent level based on the Pearson χ^2 test.

As we have done before, we can create a HypothesisTestData object from which we can extract all the properties instead of using them as arguments as we did above.

Create a HypothesisTestData object using the key combination esc scH esc to create the $\mathcal{H}$:

In[14]:= **$\mathcal{H}$ = DistributionFitTest[data, DiscreteUniformDistribution[{1, 5}], "HypothesisTestData"]**

Out[14]= HypothesisTestData[⊞   Type: DistributionFitTest   p–Value: 0.754]

Let's look at all of the available properties.

List the properties of the HypothesisTestData object:

In[15]:= $\mathcal{H}$["Properties"]

Out[15]= {AllTests, AndersonDarling, AutomaticTest, BaringhausHenze,
CramerVonMises, DegreesOfFreedom, DistanceToBoundary, FittedDistribution,
FittedDistributionParameters, HypothesisTestData, JarqueBeraALM,
KolmogorovSmirnov, Kuiper, MardiaCombined, MardiaKurtosis,
MardiaSkewness, PearsonChiSquare, Properties, PValue, PValueTable,
ShapiroWilk, ShortTestConclusion, SzekelyEnergy, TestConclusion, TestData,
TestDataTable, TestEntries, TestStatistic, TestStatisticTable, WatsonUSquare}

The "AllTests" property will list all the tests appropriate to our data and the distribution against which it is being measured.

Look at all of the appropriate tests for our data:

In[16]:= $\mathcal{H}$["AllTests"]

Out[16]= {PearsonChiSquare}

The Pearson χ^2 test of goodness of fit is indeed the appropriate test. As mentioned, we are dealing with a simple example where the probability proportions were equal. In another example, we might expect probabilities of 0.1, 0.2, 0.3, 0.25, and 0.15. In the code below, we change the p computer variable values and rerun the calculation.

Create a new probability List object:

In[17]:= p = {0.1, 0.2, 0.3, 0.25, 0.1}

Out[17]= {0.1, 0.2, 0.3, 0.25, 0.1}

Calculate a new χ^2 value:

In[18]:= chiSquare = Total[$\dfrac{(counts - n*p)^2}{n*p}$]

Out[18]= 23.5433

Calculate a new *p*-value:

In[19]:= 1 − CDF[ChiSquareDistribution[4], chiSquare]

Out[19]= 0.0000986002

A plot, similar to the previous one, visualizes the difference in p-value.

Plot the appropriate curve with the calculated χ^2 value:

In[20]:= **Plot[PDF[ChiSquareDistribution[4], x], {x, 0, 30},**
PlotLabel → "χ^2 Distribution with 4 Degrees of Freedom",
Filling → Axis, Epilog → Line[{{chiSquare, 0}, {chiSquare, 0.2}}]]

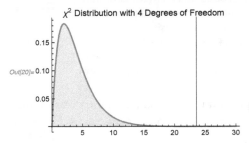

Out[20]=

In[21]:= **newDist =**
ProbabilityDistribution[{"PDF",
0.1 * Boole[x == 1] + 0.2 * Boole[x == 2] + 0.3 * Boole[x == 3] +
0.25 * Boole[x == 4] + 0.1 * Boole[x == 5]}, {x, 1, 5, 1}];

In[22]:= **DistributionFitTest[data, newDist, "TestDataTable"]**

Out[22]=

	Statistic	P-Value
Pearson χ^2	23.5433	0.0000986002

χ^2 Test of Independence

Here we want to compare the proportion of counts for two categorical variables for independence from each other. Imagine then that we have an experiment with 101 hypertensive patients (high blood pressure) and 17 non-hypertensive patients. For the sake of simplicity, we will stick to a dichotomous second categorical variable, with a participant being in group I or in group II, with 13 group I and 105 group II patients. Our null hypothesis is that the group and hypertensive variables are independent from each other, i.e. that group assignment does not influence the presence of hypertension.

Let's create a nested List object that represents the following findings for our experiment. For group I patients, we have 13 hypertensive patients and one non-hypertensive patient. In group II, we have 88 hypertensive patients and 17 non-hypertensives patients. We will store this object in the computer variable obs.

Create a nested List object to hold our experimental findings:

In[23]:= **obs = {{13, 1}, {88, 17}}**

Out[23]= {{13, 1}, {88, 17}}

Let's display it in matrix form for visual inspection.

Display the nested List object in matrix form:

In[24]:= **obs // MatrixForm**

Out[24]//MatrixForm= $\begin{pmatrix} 13 & 1 \\ 88 & 17 \end{pmatrix}$

We can use the TableForm function to make this visual inspection very illustrative. This function has a TableHeadings option. We will pass a nested List object to it. The nested List object is named rc and contains two subList objects. The first will make up our row names and the second our column names.

Create an informative table display:

In[25]:= **rc = {{"Group I", "Group II"}, {"Hypertensive", "Non–hypertensive"}};**
   TableForm[obs, TableHeadings → rc]

	Hypertensive	Non–hypertensive
Group I	13	1
Group II	88	17

Out[26]//TableForm=

The table above is named an *observed table* and, in general, such tables that count the number of cases for categorical variables are termed *contingency tables*.

Calculating simple percentages from the counts, we have 119 patients of which 84.9% are hypertensive and 11.8% are in group I. Given these percentages, we can calculate an *expected table*. For the value in row one, column one of this expected table, we look at the observed table and multiply the first row total and the first column total and divide by the overall total. That would be $14 \times 101 \div 119 = 11.9$ (see group I hypertensives in the table on page 176). Given the proportions, we would expect 11.9 group I hypertensives.

We repeat this process for each value using its respective row and column totals. This is easily done using the following code. We will store the expected table in the fit computer variable. Note that the expression of the table-in-table form with table headings is not part of the calculation. It is only done for the sake of illustrating the example. The fit nested List object is used for the actual calculation. The same goes for the use of the table form with table headings in the rest of this chapter.

Let's do all of these calculations in steps, making use of explanatory computer variable names for ease of understanding.

Calculate the total sum of patients:

In[27]:= **total = Total[Flatten[obs]]**

Out[27]= 119

Now, we calculate the fraction of hypertensive patients. This would be the sum of the values in column 1, i.e. $13 + 88$ divided by the total number of patients.

Calculate the fraction of hypertensive patients:

$$In[28]:= \text{hypertensionRatio} = \frac{\text{Total[obs〚All, 1〛]}}{\text{total}}$$

$$Out[28]= \frac{101}{119}$$

This is followed by calculating the fraction of patients in group I, i.e. $13 + 1$ divided by the total.

Calculate the fraction of patients in group I:

$$In[29]:= \text{groupIRatio} = \frac{\text{Total[obs〚1, All〛]}}{\text{total}}$$

$$Out[29]= \frac{2}{17}$$

Note that the fraction has been simplified. From here it is easy to calculate the non-hypertensive ratio (fraction) and the group II patient ratio.

Calculate the ratios:

$$In[30]:= \text{nonHypertensionRatio} = \frac{\text{Total[obs〚All, 2〛]}}{\text{total}}$$

$$Out[30]= \frac{18}{119}$$

$$In[31]:= \text{groupIIRatio} = \frac{\text{Total[obs〚2, All〛]}}{\text{total}}$$

$$Out[31]= \frac{15}{17}$$

Check if the corresponding ratios add up to 1:

```
In[32]:= {nonHypertensionRatio + hypertensionRatio, groupIIRatio + groupIRatio}
```

$$Out[32]= \{1, 1\}$$

The expected values can now be calculated. They are saved as fit:

```
In[33]:= fit = {{hypertensionRatio * groupIRatio, nonHypertensionRatio * groupIRatio},
          {hypertensionRatio * groupIIRatio,
              nonHypertensionRatio * groupIIRatio}} * total // N;
      TableForm[fit, TableHeadings → rc]
```

	Hypertensive	Non–hypertensive
Out[34]//TableForm= Group I	11.8824	2.11765
Group II	89.1176	15.8824

Now that we have values for both an observed and an expected table, we can calculate the χ^2 value. It is a rather simple equation, shown in (3), and it is based on equation (1).

$$\chi^2 = \sum_{i=1}^{n} \frac{(O_i - E_i)^2}{E_i} \tag{3}$$

Here, O_i is each individual value in our observed table and E_i is each corresponding value in the expected table. We therefore need to subtract each respective expected value from its corresponding observed value, square this difference, and divide it by the corresponding expected value. For our example, that leaves us with four values, just as in our contingency table (i.e. 2×2), and we sum all of these four values to get the χ^2 value. In the calculations that follow, we break this equation down into computational steps.

In step 1, we are interested in the difference between the observed and the expected values. We will store this in the computer variable named residual.

Calculate the difference between each corresponding observed and fitted value:

In[35]:= **residual = obs – fit;**

Express the difference in formatted-table form:

In[36]:= **TableForm[residual // N, TableHeadings → rc]**

	Hypertensive	Non–hypertensive
Out[36]//TableForm= Group I	1.11765	−1.11765
Group II	−1.11765	1.11765

In step 2, each of the values are squared and divided by the expected value. We will save this result in the χ^2array computer variable.

Calculate the differences squared and divide by the expected value for each of the four values:

In[37]:= χ**2array =** $\dfrac{\text{residual}^2}{\text{fit}}$ **;**

Express the calculations in formatted-table form:

In[38]:= **TableForm[χ2array // N, TableHeadings → rc]**

	Hypertensive	Non–hypertensive
Out[38]//TableForm= Group I	0.105125	0.589869
Group II	0.0140167	0.0786492

In step 3, the χ^2 value is the sum of all of the values above.

Use Total after flattening the nested List object:

In[39]:= χ**2 = Total[Flatten[χ2array]];**
    χ**2 // N**

Out[40]= **0.78766**

To calculate a p-value, we require a value for the degrees of freedom. We calculate it as follows, starting with the dimensions of our contingency table.

Calculate the dimensions of the contingency table:

In[41]:= **dimensions = Dimensions[obs]**

Out[41]= {2, 2}

Our 2×2 contingency table does indeed have two rows and two columns. With only two elements in our Dimensions List object, we can use the First and Last Wolfram Language functions for each of these elements.

First, Last, Part, Take, and Drop are all useful functions for manipulating List objects:

In[42]:= **First[dimensions]**

Out[42]= 2

In[43]:= **Last[dimensions]**

Out[43]= 2

In[44]:= **dof = Total[dimensions] − First[dimensions] − Last[dimensions] + 1**

Out[44]= 1

Finally, we can calculate a p-value for this statistic using CDF:

In[45]:= **1 − CDF[ChiSquareDistribution[dof], χ2] // N**

Out[45]= 0.374808

For a chosen α-value of 0.05, we cannot reject the null hypothesis, which, in the case of a χ^2 test for independence, states that the two variables are independent of each other. In the case of our experiment, that means that the presence of hypertension is independent of the group to which the patient belongs.

Fisher's Exact Test

Fisher's exact test is also used to analyze contingency tables (counts of categorical variables). It becomes particularly useful when dealing with small sample sizes but can, in essence, be used for large sample sizes as well.

Do not be fooled by the term *exact*. It does not mean that we get a p-value that is somehow superior to other statistical tests such as the χ^2 test of independence. It simply refers to the fact that the p-value can be calculated directly instead of using a test statistic, as we have been doing up to now.

Although methods exist that allow for the use of large contingency tables, it is perhaps best to use the χ^2 test of independence in these circumstances. The standard method for using the Fisher's exact test calls for a 2×2 contingency table.

Imagine then that we have a 4×4 contingency table with unique sample space data point value counts for two categorical variables as shown below.

A 4×4 contingency table:

In[46]:= **obs = {{1, 2, 0, 0}, {1, 0, 0, 1}, {2, 3, 1, 0}, {1, 0, 0, 1}};**
obs // MatrixForm

Out[47]//MatrixForm=
$$\begin{pmatrix} 1 & 2 & 0 & 0 \\ 1 & 0 & 0 & 1 \\ 2 & 3 & 1 & 0 \\ 1 & 0 & 0 & 1 \end{pmatrix}$$

These could represent four sets of individuals (groups A through D), choosing between four answers (I through IV) for a survey question. Let's use the TableForm function to better illustrate our hypothetical example.

Create a visual table representation:

In[48]:= **TableForm[obs,**
TableHeadings → {{"Group A", "Group B", "Group C", "Group D"}, {"I", "II", "III", "IV"}}]

	I	II	III	IV
Group A	1	2	0	0
Group B	1	0	0	1
Group C	2	3	1	0
Group D	1	0	0	1

Out[48]//TableForm=

These are small numbers indeed. The χ^2 distribution might not give an accurate calculation for the p-value in this example. By mutual agreement and specific to the research in this case, the researchers could reduce this continency table to a 2×2 table by grouping, for instance, the subjects in groups A and B and then C and D and then by grouping the answer selections into S (for I and II) and T (for III and IV). The contingency table would then look like the next table.

New contingency table:

In[49]:= **newObs = {{4, 1}, {6, 2}};**
TableForm[newObs, TableHeadings → {{"Group A and B", "Group C and D"}, {"S", "T"}}]

	S	T
Group A and B	4	1
Group C and D	6	2

Out[50]//TableForm=

This was achieved by simply summing the counts in each of the original contingency table values.

In order to understand the equation for the *p*-value, we will use the following table.

Generic table:

In[51]:= **TableForm[{{a, b}, {c, d}},**
       TableHeadings → {{"Group A and B", "Group C and D"}, {"S", "T"}}]

Out[51]//TableForm=
	S	T
Group A and B	a	b
Group C and D	c	d

For a total of *n* participants, we have $n = a + b + c + d$, the equation for the directly calculated and therefore exact *p*-value is then shown in equation (4) below.

$$p = \frac{(a + b)! \, (c + d)! \, (a + c)! \, (b + d)!}{a! \, b! \, c! \, d! \, n!} \tag{4}$$

Here, the exclamation mark (!) means *factorial*. Factorial is a way of multiplying all the counting numbers below a given number with the number itself, i.e. $3 != 3 \times 2 \times 1 = 6$ and $4 != 4 \times 3 \times 2 \times 1 = 24$. These numbers get big very quickly. (Always remember that $0 != 1$ and $1 != 1$.)

Calculate the factorial of 0 and the first 10 natural numbers:

In[52]:= **Factorial[Range[1, 10]]**

Out[52]= {1, 2, 6, 24, 120, 720, 5040, 40 320, 362 880, 3 628 800}

If we plot the factorial against the exponential, we see how quickly it grows. In fact, in the next plot, the exponential barely leaves the *x* axis.

Factorial versus exponential growth (just for fun):

In[53]:= **ListLinePlot[{Factorial[Range[1, 10]], Exp[Range[1, 10]]}, PlotRange → All,**
       PlotLabel → "Growth", PlotLabels → {"Factorial", "Exponential"}]

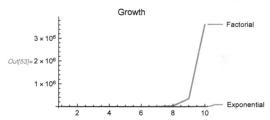

Using the Wolfram Language Factorial function, we would thus calculate the *p*-value.

Calculate the *p*-value:

In[54]:= **(Factorial[5] * Factorial[8] * Factorial[10] * Factorial[3]) /**
       (Factorial[4] * Factorial[1] * Factorial[6] * Factorial[2] * Factorial[13]) // N

Out[54]= 0.48951

There you have it. Create your own List objects and have fun analyzing categorical variables.

Exercises

13.1 Create a contingency table for an experiment in which there are two groups (rows), each with three conditions (columns) such that the first row has values 87, 101, 31 and the second 88, 29, 99. Save this as the computer variable **obs**. This could represent the counts for an experiment in which there are two groups (unique data point values for a variable called Group) and three possible outcomes (unique data point values for a variable called Response).

13.2 Express this contingency table in TableForm with row headers *GroupA* and *GroupB* and column headers *ResponseA*, *ResponseB*, and *ResponseC*. First save these as table headings in the computer variable **rc** and then print the table to the screen.

13.3 Calculate a table of expected values and store it in the computer variable **fit**. Print this to the screen without table headings.

13.4 Calculate the difference between each of the six observed and expected values and save it in the computer variable **residual**. Print this table to the screen.

13.5 Calculate a table of squared differences divided by each respective expected value. Save the table in the computer variable *χ*2array and print it to the screen.

13.6 Calculate the χ^2 value and save it in the computer variable *χ*2. Print the value to the screen.

13.7 Calculate the degrees of freedom and save to the computer variable **dof**.

13.8 Calculate the *p*-value for this χ^2 value.

13.9 Consider an experiment in which there are only nine participants. They can be divided into two groups, A and B, and two responses, I and II, such that there are two I's and two II's in group A and four I's and one II in group B (given below). Calculate a *p*-value for this experiment using Fisher's exact test.

$$\begin{pmatrix} 2 & 2 \\ 4 & 1 \end{pmatrix}$$

More to Explore

A good overview of the various functions in the documentation on hypothesis tests (wolfr.am/HypothesisTests)

Try this excellent Demonstration by C. Boucher on hypothesis tests and population mean (wolfr.am/PopulationMean)

An advanced read on Cauchy distributions by J. Vrbik in *The Mathematica Journal* (wolfr.am/cauchy-example)

14 | Nonparametric Tests

In the chapters on parametric tests, correlation, and linear regression, we made use of tests based on some assumptions of the distribution of parameters in the population from which sample subjects were taken. In this chapter, we take a look at statistical tests that can be used when these assumptions are not met.

We will start with considering the use of the Student t test by looking at the assumptions that we discussed in Chapter 10. We will use List objects with data point values that do not meet the assumptions for the use of parametric tests and introduce the nonparametric alternative, namely the Mann–Whitney U-test.

From here, we will move on to the sign test. Initially, we will work through all of the individual steps needed for this test, which will serve as an example of how nonparametric tests work. After that, we will perform the same test in one step using the built-in function SignTest. For the rest of the tests, we will skip the step-by-step creation and concentrate on the Wolfram Language implementations.

When Assumptions Are Not Met

The two notable assumptions for the use of parametric tests that we have discussed are (1) the normal distribution of the variable in the underlying population and (2) the lack of outliers.

In this chapter, we will create List objects of variables that do not meet these assumptions. In the following code cells, we create two List objects of a single variable for two groups. We will ensure that the values are not from a normal distribution by specifying the χ^2 distribution.

List object for a variable in group A:

```
In[1]:= SeedRandom[123]
       groupA = RandomVariate[ChiSquareDistribution[2], 100];
```

List object for a variable in group B:

In[3]:= **SeedRandom[123]**
groupB = RandomVariate[ChiSquareDistribution[3], 100] − 1;

To investigate the assumptions for the use of parametric tests, we take a look at the q-q plots and the Shapiro–Wilk test results for comparison with respect to the normal distribution. We also create box-and-whisker plots to identify possible outliers in the data values for the two List objects.

q-q plot of group A:

In[5]:= **QuantilePlot[groupA, NormalDistribution[],**
PlotLabel → "Quantile–Quantile Plot for Group A"]

Out[5]=
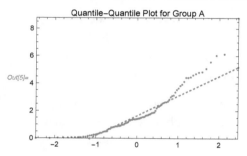

q-q plot of group B:

In[6]:= **QuantilePlot[groupB, NormalDistribution[],**
PlotLabel → "Quantile–Quantile Plot for Group B"]

Out[6]=
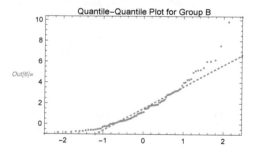

The *p*-value for the Shapiro–Wilk test for group A:

In[7]:= **ShapiroWilkTest[groupA]**

Out[7]= 1.01753×10^{-7}

The *p*-value for the Shapiro–Wilk test for group B:

In[8]:= **ShapiroWilkTest[groupB]**

Out[8]= 2.09876×10^{-7}

Box-and-whisker plot with outliers:

In[9]:= **BoxWhiskerChart[{Labeled[groupA, "Group A"], Labeled[groupB, "Group B"]},**
   "Outliers", PlotLabel → "Outliers"]

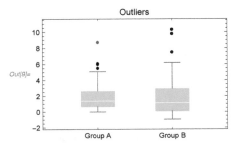

Out[9]=

We can clearly see from the q-q plots that neither of the lists follows a normal distribution. This is confirmed by the p-values of the Shapiro–Wilk tests, which for both groups are smaller than a chosen α-value of 0.05. We also note for the box-and-whisker plots that there are various outliers.

Our goal is to compare the data between the two groups that we created. Even though we have not met the assumptions for the use of a parametric test such as the Student t test, it can still be performed. Let's have a look at the summary statistics of the two List objects and then compare their means by calculating a p-value using the Student t test.

We calculate the means for the two List objects using the Mean function and the shorthand notation /@ to apply the function to the nested List objects that follow. We will also use //N to get a numerical result.

Calculate the means:

In[10]:= **Mean /@ {groupA, groupB} // N**

Out[10]= {1.86625, 1.77882}

We note a mean for group A of 1.87 and a mean of 1.78 for group B. Let's have a look at the median and standard deviation for each List object.

Calculate the medians:

In[11]:= **Median /@ {groupA, groupB} // N**

Out[11]= {1.42582, 1.16887}

Calculate the standard deviations:

In[12]:= **StandardDeviation /@ {groupA, groupB} // N**

Out[12]= {1.67295, 2.24745}

There is a relatively large difference between the groups with respect to the median. Now we perform the Student t test to compare the means. We use the VerifyTestAssumptions argument and set it to None so that the Wolfram Language does not check for the parametric test assumptions.

Student t test for comparison of means:

In[13]:= **TTest[{groupA, groupB}, VerifyTestAssumptions → None]**

Out[13]= **0.755324**

We note a p-value of larger than a chosen α-value of 0.05, which we would term an insignificant difference. We would therefore fail to reject the null hypothesis and conclude that there is no difference for our numerical variable under consideration when compared between the two groups.

This would not be a proper test to conduct, though, since we have violated the assumptions for the use of this test. The nonparametric alternative to the Student t test is the Mann–Whitney U-test.

Mann–Whitney U-Test

The Mann-Whitney U-test compares the medians of two lists of values. In the code cell below, we use the MannWhitneyTest function. The first argument is a nested List object containing our two List objects. The second argument of 0 denotes testing whether the medians are equal. Lastly, we ask for a table that will give us both the test statistic and a p-value of our data.

Use the MannWhitneyTest function to compare the medians:

In[14]:= **MannWhitneyTest[{groupA, groupB}, 0, "TestDataTable"]**

Out[14]=

	Statistic	P-Value
Mann–Whitney	5482.	0.239398

With our chosen sample values, the p-value is now very different to the Student t test p-value. It is still larger than a chosen α-value of 0.05 and we fail to reject our null hypothesis that there is a difference in the median values between the two groups.

Although it has been shown that the nonparametric tests are less sensitive at detecting a true difference between samples, their use is encouraged when the assumptions for the use of the parametric tests are not met.

To finish this section, note that we can also use the LocationTest function. The Wolfram Language will determine which tests are appropriate for our data.

Use the LocationTest function so that Mathematica can decide on the best test to use:

In[15]:= **LocationTest[{groupA, groupB}, 0, "TestDataTable"]**

Out[15]=

	Statistic	P-Value
Mann-Whitney	5482.	0.239398

The Wolfram Language indeed correctly chose the Mann–Whitney U-test.

Sign Test

The sign test can be used in place of the paired-sample t test. This means that the sign test is designed to be used when the two List objects representing the same variable for two samples are not independent. For example, we might look at the data point values for the same variable before and after an intervention. The sign test compares the sign (positive, negative, or the same) resulting from the difference between each pair of values. The magnitude of the difference is of no consequence, only the sign of the difference. All data point value pairs that are equal are discarded.

The sign test can also be used as a nonparametric alternative to the one-sample t test. One list will then contain the same value for all of its elements. It can also be used when dealing with ordinal categorical variables, where it would be inappropriate to consider such data point values as numerical.

In the next code cell, we create two List objects to use for the sign test. These represent the test results for 17 subjects before and after an intervention. Our interest lies in whether the results after the intervention were lower than before the intervention. The null hypothesis will be that there is no difference between the two sets of data, i.e. there are just as many that were lower after the intervention than there were values that were higher after the intervention. The alternative hypothesis would be that there are more values that are lower after the intervention. This is a one-tailed alternative hypothesis. Let's collect our data.

Create two lists representing our before and after data for the same set of subjects:

In[16]:= **before = {3, 3, 5, 4, 4, 5, 5, 5, 3, 4, 5, 4, 4, 5, 5, 5, 1};**
after = {4, 4, 4, 3, 4, 4, 4, 4, 4, 3, 1, 1, 2, 4, 2, 1, 4};

In the next step, we count how many of the after data point values were actually less than the before values. The MapThread function will compare each element of the two lists in pair-wise fashion and return a Boolean value, i.e. True or False. The Counts function will tell us how many times each occurred.

We have to be careful how we order the List objects. Since we use the Less argument, we list after and then before to indicate that we want to know if the after data point value was less than the before data point value for each pair. (We could also have used Greater and changed the order of the List objects.)

The MapThread function compares the before and after values:

In[18]:= **MapThread[Less, {after, before}]**

Out[18]= {False, False, True, True, False, True, True,
  True, False, True, True, True, True, True, True, True, False}

If we consider the first point with a value of 3 before and a value of 4 after, we do indeed see a Boolean value of False, since 4 is not less than 3. We now pass the previous calculation as argument to the Counts function to count the Boolean values.

Wrap the MapThread function in the Counts function:

In[19]:= **Counts[MapThread[Less, {after, before}]]**

Out[19]= <| False → 5, True → 12 |>

We note that in five cases the after data point value was not less than the before value. While it might not have been less than, it might have been equal to and, therefore, we need to find out if any of the paired data point values were equal.

Check for equal values:

In[20]:= **Counts[MapThread[Equal, {before, after}]]**

Out[20]= <| False → 16, True → 1 |>

There was indeed one data point pair that was equal. So, we have four cases in which the after was greater than the before and 12 in which it was less. In terms of the name of this test, we would have four positively signed values if we subtracted the after from the before and 12 negatively signed values. The question is: Is this a difference that will force us to reject our null hypothesis?

The solution is akin to tossing a coin. It has a probability of landing heads up of 0.5, the same as for tails. With one instance being equal, we ended up with 16 trials. In four of them, the after data point values were greater than the before data point values, i.e. the sign of the values were positive.

This means that we can use the binomial distribution with a probability of success (a positive value) being 0.5. We can use the CDF function noting four positive results. The BinomialDistrubution function takes two arguments. The first is the number of trials or sample size. This is 16 in our instance. The second is the probability of success (positive signs), which is 0.5.

Calculate the one-tailed p-value:

In[21]:= **CDF[BinomialDistribution[16, 0.5], 4]**

Out[21]= 0.0384064

The Wolfram Language provides the SignTest function. In the code cell below, we use it to indicate that we require a one-tailed alternative hypothesis. In order to do this, we must list the after List object first.

Calculate the sign test:

```
In[22]:= SignTest[{after, before}, 0, "TestDataTable", AlternativeHypothesis → "Less"]
```

	Statistic	P-Value
Sign	4	0.0384064

Out[22]=

We can now reject our null hypothesis since we have a p-value of less than a chosen α-value of 0.05, thereby accepting our alternative hypothesis. The alternative hypothesis stated that there were more values that were lower after the intervention.

Be very careful when using the SignTest function and consider how the alternative hypothesis is structured as it also defines the null hypothesis. It is all too easy to use the List objects in the incorrect order of comparison.

Wilcoxon Signed Rank Test

As with the sign test, the Wilcoxon signed rank sum test, or the Wilcoxon test for short, can be used as a nonparametric alternative to the paired-sample t test and the one-sample t test, as well as for cases with ordinal categorical variables.

Not only do we use the sign of the difference between pairs of data point values (or between the data point values and a set median as in the case of a one-sample test), but we also rank the differences and sum them, allowing the calculation of the W-statistic. This is a more robust test than the sign test.

We can apply this test to similar before and after data for the same variable as we used in the sign test. The Wolfram Language function is SignedRankTest. We once again create two List objects to simulate before and after data point values, simulating an experiment where our variable of investigation was measured before and after an intervention.

Create two new List objects:

```
before = {86, 71, 77, 68, 91, 72, 77, 91, 70, 71, 88, 87};
after = {88, 72, 69, 64, 96, 72, 65, 90, 65, 70, 81, 84};
```

We can visualize the difference using the BarChart function.

A bar chart of the differences:

BarChart[after − before, PlotLabel → "Differences between the before and after Values"]

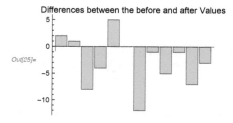

We note that in eight cases, the **after** value was less than the **before** value for each pair of values.

In the code cell below, we state that, according to our null hypothesis the difference between the medians is 0 and that we require both the W-statistic and a two-tailed alternative hypothesis p-value.

A two-tailed Wilcoxon signed rank sum test:

In[26]:= **SignedRankTest[{before, after}, 0, "TestDataTable"]**

Out[26]=
	Statistic	P-Value
Signed-Rank	52.5	0.0903613

The p-value is larger than a chosen α-value of 0.05 and we fail to reject our null hypothesis.

What about one-tailed alternative hypotheses? Before we go any further, let's have a look at the median values for each List object since nonparametric tests compare the medians.

Find the medians for the before and after samples using shorthand notation:

In[27]:= **Median /@ {before, after} // N**

Out[27]= **{77., 72.}**

Find the means for the before and after samples using shorthand notation:

In[28]:= **Mean /@ {before, after} // N**

Out[28]= **{79.0833, 76.3333}**

The median has decreased and, as we suspected, so has the mean. Now, let's suggest that we were testing a new intervention for which we hypothesize that the values would decrease after the intervention. In keeping with hypothesis testing, the null hypothesis would be that the **after** values are equal to or larger than the **before** values and our alternative hypothesis states that the median for the **after** values are less than the median for the **before** values. In the next code cell, we state the alternative hypothesis with a lesser value for the AlternativeHypothesis argument. Let's calculate a p-value.

An alternative hypothesis for a decrease in after:

In[29]:= **SignedRankTest[{after, before}, 0, AlternativeHypothesis → "Less"]**

Out[29]= 0.0451807

With an α-value of 0.05, we reject the null hypothesis and accept the alternative hypothesis. We have shown that the intervention significantly decreases the after values.

It bears mentioning again that we have to be careful how the null and alternative hypotheses are stated. It determines the order in which we place the List objects and crucially, the choice of difference for the AlthenativeHypothesis argument.

Kruskal–Wallis Test

The Kruskal–Wallis test is the nonparametric test of choice when we cannot use one-way analysis of variance to compare the means of more than two groups.

So as to have data that does not follow a normal distribution, we will once again use the χ^2 distribution with the RandomVariate function to create three random samples, each with 60 random values.

Instead of creating the three List objects that represent our three groups separately, we can create a nested List object. The Wolfram Language statistical test function will take either form (List objects or nested List objects) as argument.

Create our three random groups:

In[30]:= **SeedRandom[123]**
lists = RandomVariate[ChiSquareDistribution[2], {3, 60}];

Our first order of business is to summarize the data. We will do so by looking at the mean and median values of each of the three groups.

Use shorthand notation to calculate the three means:

In[32]:= **Mean /@ lists**

Out[32]= {1.90629, 1.80026, 2.18371}

Use shorthand notation to calculate the three medians:

In[33]:= **Median /@ lists**

Out[33]= {1.44407, 1.3467, 1.44108}

Now we can test for the assumptions required for the use of parametric tests. We begin by looking at q-q plots for each of the three groups.

Use shorthand notation to create three q-q plots:

In[34]:= **QuantilePlot /@ lists**

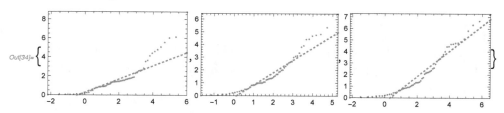

As suspected, we note that the data point values do not follow along the normal line. To confirm our suspicions, we can conduct the Shapiro–Wilk test on each of the lists.

Calculate a *p*-value for each of the three groups:

In[35]:= **ShapiroWilkTest /@ lists**

Out[35]= $\{1.04092 \times 10^{-6}, 0.0000640231, 0.0000868137\}$

All three groups have very small *p*-values. We can therefore reject the hypothesis that the data point values for the samples came from a population in which our variable of interest was normally distributed.

As a final test of the assumptions for the use of parametric tests, let's consider any outliers with the use of a box-and-whisker plot.

A box-and-whisker plot of the three groups:

In[36]:= **BoxWhiskerChart[lists, "Outliers", PlotLabel → "Three Groups"]**

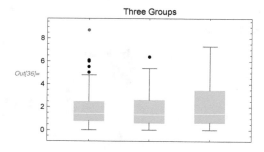

There are numerous outliers for the first two groups.

The Wolfram Language function that performs nonparametric tests for more than two groups is **LocationEquivalenceTest**. In the next code cell, we specify that we require the test statistic and the *p*-value and ask for the Kruskal–Wallis test by name.

Conduct the Kruskal–Wallis test:

In[37]:= **LocationEquivalenceTest[lists, {"TestDataTable", "KruskalWallis"}]**

Out[37]=

	Statistic	P-Value
Kruskal-Wallis	0.563254	0.756601

We fail to reject a null hypothesis that there is a difference between the three groups.

This might not be the only test that the Wolfram Language will consider given the sample data. Instead of specifying the Kruskal–Wallis test, we can also call for all tests using the All argument.

Call for all appropriate tests:

In[38]:= **LocationEquivalenceTest[lists, {"TestDataTable", All}]**

Out[38]=

	Statistic	P-Value
Friedman Rank	0.346186	0.708097
Kruskal-Wallis	0.563254	0.756601

In this case, the Friedman rank test was added.

As with most of the statistical tests in the Wolfram Language, we can create a HypothesisTestData object. This allows for the extraction of many more properties than just the test statistic and *p*-value that we have been using throughout this chapter.

Create a HypothesisTestData object:

In[39]:= $\mathcal{H}$ **= LocationEquivalenceTest[lists, "HypothesisTestData"]**

Out[39]= HypothesisTestData[⊞ 〽 Type: LocationEquivalenceTest
p–Value: 0.757]

Let's have a look at all the properties that are available in this object.

Properties of the HypothesisTestData object:

In[40]:= $\mathcal{H}$**["Properties"]**

Out[40]= {AllTests, AutomaticTest, CompleteBlockF, DegreesOfFreedom,
FriedmanRank, HypothesisTestData, KruskalWallis, KSampleT,
Properties, PValue, PValueTable, ShortTestConclusion, TestConclusion,
TestData, TestDataTable, TestEntries, TestStatistic, TestStatisticTable}

We notice the "TestDataTable" that provides us with the usual test statistic and the *p*-value. Let's look at some of the other properties. We will start with the degrees of freedom. This will show us the number of groups minus 1 and the total number of data point values minus the number of groups.

Degrees of freedom:

In[41]:= $\mathcal{H}$**["DegreesOfFreedom"]**

Out[41]= {2, 177}

"TestConclusion" is always fun to use and can help us with writing a report of our analysis.

A written conclusion of the test result:

In[42]:= $\mathcal{H}$["TestConclusion"] // TraditionalForm

Out[42]//TraditionalForm=

> The null hypothesis that the mean are equal
> is not rejected at the 5 percent level based on the Kruskal-Wallis test.

Exercises

14.1 Create two List objects named groupI and groupII. For groupI, use a random seed of 1234 to create 100 data point values for a random choice of integers in the domain 90 through 110. For the groupII data point values, add a random integer in the domain −10 to 10 to each of the values in groupI using a similar random seed.

14.2 Create q-q plots for the two List objects using /@ shorthand notation.

14.3 Test for normality and calculate the p-value for the Shapiro–Wilk test for each of the List objects.

14.4 Create a box-and-whisker plot for each of the two List objects.

14.5 Since the p-values were less than a chosen α-value of 0.05, use the Mann–Whitney U-test specifying a 0 difference in medians and express it as a test data table.

14.6 Create a third set of data point values, named groupIII, to simulate a third group. Use a similar random seed as above to create 100 random integer values in the domain 100 through 140.

14.7 Create a q-q plot for groupIII.

14.8 Calculate a p-value for groupIII using the Shapiro–Wilk test.

14.9 Create a box-and-whisker plot of groupIII.

14.10 Create a nested List object of the three sets of data point values using the Table function. Name this List object lists.

14.11 Calculate a test statistic and p-value for lists using the Kruskal–Wallis test.

More to Explore

Find the interval where the null hypothesis cannot be rejected with this Demonstration by O. E. Prokopchenko (wolfr.am/SamplingStatistics)

Try this excellent Demonstration by C. Boucher on hypothesis tests and population mean in the Wolfram Cloud (wolfr.am/PopulationMean)

The Documentation Center has a substantial section on the Mann–Whitney test (wolfr.am/MannWhitney)

15 | A Research Project Demonstration

In this chapter, we consider a research project with simulated data. The aim is to bring together all of the knowledge in the previous chapters. This chapter also serves as an example of a computational essay. This forms the basis of research projects in many research institutions. A computational essay, such as what we create with a Mathematica notebook is the ideal format to share statistical analysis with individuals in a research group. A notebook allows for rich content including stylized text, computation, and the output of the computation.

The Research Question

Statistical analysis follows data collection, which is preceded by a research question. The scientific method and inferential statistics shown in this book are based on a hypothesis question.

A research question must be stated clearly, such that we can have a null and an alternative hypothesis.

Most research projects will have more than one research question. Some have a main research question with one or more secondary questions.

In the example for this chapter, we consider two groups of patients. All the subjects in this simulated project are admitted with airway disease. Group A subjects are admitted with chronic obstructive airway disease (COAD) and group B with chronic bronchitis (CB). For the sake of argument, we will assume that there are no confounding factors and no bias in the selection of the subjects.

Our primary research question is whether there is a difference in in-hospital mortality between these two groups. In health-care research literature, in-hospital mortality refers to death occurring in the hospital during the admission of the patients. Our null hypothesis is that there is no difference between the groups and our alternative hypothesis is that there is a difference.

How would we measure our research questions though? How do we measure mortality? Well, mortality is a nominal categorical variable with a sample space of "Yes" and "No". A subject either died in the hospital or they did not.

Our secondary research questions will look at differences between the following variables:

1. Age
2. Correlation between overall admission lactate levels and white cell counts

We will look at the definition of these variables, their sample space, and the hypotheses for each question when we analyze these questions.

The Data Import

We take for granted that this notebook and the spreadsheet file containing our data is located in the same folder.

We start by setting the working directory:

In[1]:= **SetDirectory[NotebookDirectory[]];**

The data exists in a spreadsheet saved as a comma-separated values (.cvs) file named *SimulatedData.csv*.

Use the SemanticImport function to import the data file:

In[2]:= **data = SemanticImport["SimulatedData.csv"];**

Let's inspect the Dataset object to see that it imported correctly and how many subjects and variables it contains.

View the first five rows using Part notation, ⟦...⟧:

In[3]:= **data⟦ ;; 5⟧**

	Group	Age	BMI	SOB	Shock	MechanicalVentilation	Lactate
	COAD	70	21	Mild	Yes	Yes	42
	CB	66	33	Moderate	No	Yes	54
Out[3]=	COAD	69	29	Severe	No	Yes	34
	COAD	40	28	Moderate	Yes	Yes	50
	COAD	61	31	Moderate	Yes	Yes	53

Use the Dimensions function to interrogate the number of subjects and the number of variables (columns):

In[4]:= **Dimensions[data]**

Out[4]= **{120, 9}**

There are 120 subjects and eight variables. The "Group" variable contains the data point values that we will use to separate the patients into groups A and B.

Use Dataset object notation to count the number of individuals in each group:

In[5]:= **data[Tally, "Group"]**

Out[5]=

COAD	56
CB	64

We are ready to start answering our research questions.

The Primary Research Question

Our primary research question involves a difference in mortality rate between the two groups. We can answer this question by looking at independence between these variables, i.e. a χ^2 test for independence. Our null hypothesis is that these two variables are independent and our alternative hypothesis is that they are indeed dependent.

In order to conduct this test, we need a table of observed values:

In[6]:= **data[GroupBy["Group"], Tally, "InHospitalMortality"]**

Out[6]=

COAD	No	38
	Yes	18
CB	Yes	20
	No	44

We will follow the steps shown in Chapter 13 on comparing categorical variables.

Create a table of observed values as a nested List object:

In[7]:= **obs = {{18, 38}, {20, 44}}**

Out[7]= {{18, 38}, {20, 44}}

Create row and column values to aid in reading the table. COAD refers to chronic obstructive airway disease and CB refers to chronic bronchitis:

In[8]:= **rc = {{"COAD", "CB"}, {"Died", "Survived"}}**

Out[8]= {{COAD, CB}, {Died, Survived}}

View the contingency table:

In[9]:= **TableForm[obs, TableHeadings → rc]**

Out[9]//TableForm=
	Died	Survived
COAD	18	38
CB	20	44

We now create our expected table (a table of expected values given the data):

In[10]:= **fit = Outer[Times, Plus @@@ obs, Plus @@@ Transpose[obs]] / Length[data]**

Out[10]= $\left\{\left\{\frac{266}{15}, \frac{574}{15}\right\}, \left\{\frac{304}{15}, \frac{656}{15}\right\}\right\}$

View the expected table in table form:

In[11]:= **TableForm[fit, TableHeadings → rc] // N**

Out[11]//TableForm=
	Died	Survived
COAD	17.7333	38.2667
CB	20.2667	43.7333

Next, we complete the calculation of the residuals, the χ^2 array, and the degrees of freedom in order to calculate the p-value.

Calculate the residuals:

In[12]:= **residual = obs − fit**

Out[12]= $\left\{\left\{\frac{4}{15}, -\frac{4}{15}\right\}, \left\{-\frac{4}{15}, \frac{4}{15}\right\}\right\}$

Calculate the χ^2 array:

In[13]:= χ**2Array** $= \dfrac{\text{residual}^2}{\text{fit}}$

Out[13]= $\left\{\left\{\frac{8}{1995}, \frac{8}{4305}\right\}, \left\{\frac{1}{285}, \frac{1}{615}\right\}\right\}$

Calculate the degrees of freedom:

In[14]:= **dof = Length[Flatten[obs]] − Length[obs] − Length[Transpose[obs]] + 1**

Out[14]= 1

Now we calculate a χ^2 value given our χ^2 array:

In[15]:= χ**2 = Plus @@ Flatten[χ2Array];**
χ**2 // N**

Out[16]= 0.0110031

Finally, we calculate the area under the curve for our χ^2 value given a χ^2 distribution for a single degree of freedom.

Use CDF and ChiSquareDistribution to calculate the area under the curve (*p*-value):

In[17]:= **1 − CDF[ChiSquareDistribution[dof], χ2] // N**

Out[17]= **0.916459**

If we look at the plot below, we get an intuition of our large *p*-value. It shows part of the graph of a χ^2 distribution with one degree of freedom (the probability distribution function). We also see a vertical line at our χ^2 value. The area under the curve that we are interested in lies to the right of this line. It is easy to see that this is the majority of the area under the curve.

Plotting ChiSquareDistribution is easy, note axes settings and label naming:

In[18]:= **Show[Plot[PDF[ChiSquareDistribution[1], x], {x, 0, 0.4}, PlotRange → {0, 5},**
   PlotLabel → "χ^2 Distribution for a Single Degree of Freedom",
   AxesLabel → {"x", "Probability Density"}], Graphics[Line[{{χ2, 0}, {χ2, 5}}]]]

Out[18]=

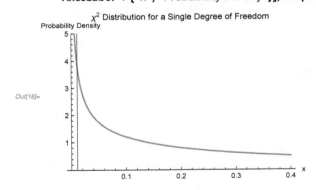

We can now finally write the following in our research manuscript: A total number of 38 (31.7%) patients succumbed during their hospital admission, 18 (32.1%) deaths for those with COAD and 20 (31.3%) for those with CB. There was, therefore, no significant difference in mortality between these two groups (χ^2 0.01, *p* 0.92).

Our secondary research questions are waiting.

A Difference in Age between the Two Groups

Age is a continuous numerical variable. The null hypothesis is that there is no difference between the mean ages for the two groups and the alternative hypothesis is that there is a difference in the mean values. Since we are comparing two independent groups, we can use the Student *t* test. This is a parametric test, and we need to check the assumptions for its use.

Our first port of call, though, is to summarize our data using descriptive statistics.

Use the GroupBy function and then a list of summary statistics:

In[19]:= **data[GroupBy["Group"],**
{Min, Max, Mean, Median, StandardDeviation, InterquartileRange}, "Age"]

Out[19]=

COAD	18	74	45.8571	47	17.6825	63/2
CB	19	77	50.4375	53	17.6373	67/2

To visualize the data, a box-and-whisker chart will be appropriate. We can divide our Dataset object by the sample space elements of the "Group" variable.

Use the Select function to create two unique Dataset objects:

In[20]:= **coad = data[Select[#Group == "COAD" &]];**
cb = data[Select[#Group == "CB" &]];

By setting these definitions, we can then extract two separate List objects to hold all the age values for each group.

Use the List function to extract List objects:

In[22]:= **coadAge = Normal[coad[List, "Age"]]〚1〛;**
cbAge = Normal[cb[List, "Age"]]〚1〛;

We are now ready to create our data visualization.

Use the BoxWhiskerChart function to visualize the data. Add a plot label and chart labels:

In[24]:= **BoxWhiskerChart[{coadAge, cbAge}, "Outliers",**
PlotLabel → "Age Difference between Two Groups", ChartLabels → {"COAD", "CB"}]

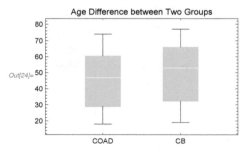

For a quick look at the two distributions, we can group the original Dataset object by the "Group" variable and plot the two histograms.

By clicking on one of the two histograms, a detailed version of it will appear.

Use Slot notation, ⊞, to add a title and axes labels:

In[25]:= **data[GroupBy["Group"], Histogram[⊞, PlotLabel → "Distribution of Ages",**
      AxesLabel → {"Age Bracket", "Count"}] &, "Age"]

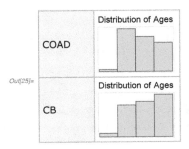

Out[25]=

We can also create a histogram that shows both sets of ages with appropriate legends.

In[26]:= **Histogram[{coadAge, cbAge}, ChartLegends → {"COAD", "CB"},**
      AxesLabel → {"Age Bracket", "Count"}]

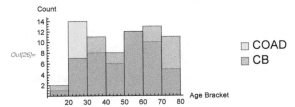

Out[26]=

The data does not seem normally distributed. The Shapiro–Wilk test provides us with a probability that the data was taken from an underlying population in which the variable is normally distributed.

Use the ShapiroWilkTest function to test for the assumption of normality:

In[27]:= **ShapiroWilkTest /@ {coadAge, cbAge}**

Out[27]= {0.00102087, 0.00175643}

Note the significant results for both groups (p-values less than 0.05). This means we fail the assumptions for the use of a parametric test. We will, therefore, use a nonparametric alternative.

Use the Mann–Whitney U-test to compare the two ages:

In[28]:= **MannWhitneyTest[{coadAge, cbAge}]**

Out[28]= 0.147867

Since we used a nonparametric test, we were actually comparing median values. We will express these next, together with the minimum and maximum ages.

Calculate the overall median (we have already calculated the median for the two groups):

In[29]:= **N @ data[Median, "Age"]**

Out[29]= 51.5

Given all of our previous analysis, we can now state the following in our research manuscript: The overall median age was 51.5 years with the youngest patient being 18 and the oldest being 77. For the patients with COAD, the median age was 47 years (min 18, max 74). This was not significantly different from the CB group, with a median age of 53 years (min 19, max 77) ($p = 0.14$).

A Correlation between Lactate and White Blood Cell Count

Here we are looking at two different numerical variables: lactate and white cell count. Each subject in our dataset will have a value for each of the variables. Our aim is to see whether these *pairs* of values are correlated, if there is a change in one as the other changes.

The null hypothesis for this research question is that there is no correlation between the two variables and the alternative hypothesis is that there is a correlation between them. As always, we set an α-value of 0.05.

This question is answered by a correlation test. The result is the Pearson correlation coefficient, r. In Chapter 11, we calculated r, the 95% confidence interval around r, and a p-value for this result. We learned that the correlation coefficient does not follow a normal distribution. In this chapter, though, we will use the fact that the Wolfram Language assumes r to asymptotically follow the Student t distribution for a degree of freedom equal to the sample size minus 2. This allows us to make use of the PearsonCorrelationTest function and saves us some time in calculating the results that we require. As always, though, we start by describing and visualizing the data to get a better intuition for the results.

Use Mean, StandardDeviation, Min, Max, Median, and InterquartileRange to calculate the summary statistics of the "Lactate" and "WCC" variables:

In[30]:= **N[Normal[**
**   data[{Mean, StandardDeviation, Min, Max, Median, InterquartileRange}, "Lactate"]]]**

Out[30]= {49.925, 9.30994, 27., 77., 50., 13.}

In[31]:= **N[Normal[**
**   data[{Mean, StandardDeviation, Min, Max, Median, InterquartileRange}, "WCC"]]]**

Out[31]= {11.7783, 1.2907, 8.3, 15.4, 11.8, 1.55}

Use the Histogram function to plot the frequency distribution of the "Lactate" and "WCC" variables:

In[32]:= **data[Histogram[#, PlotLabel → "Frequency Distribution of Lactate Levels"] &, "Lactate"]**

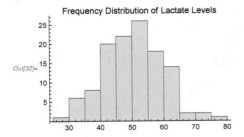

In[33]:= **data[Histogram[#, PlotLabel → "Frequency Distribution of Lactate Levels"] &, "WCC"]**

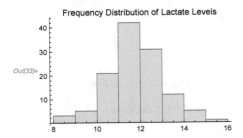

Both of these variables seem to be almost normally distributed. Let's investigate the assumption of normality by using an appropriate test.

Extract two List objects for the two variables using the Normal function:

In[34]:= **lactate = Normal[data[List, "Lactate"]]⟦1⟧;**
wcc = Normal[data[List, "WCC"]]⟦1⟧;

Use the ShapiroWilkTest function to test for the assumption of normality:

In[36]:= **ShapiroWilkTest /@ {lactate, wcc}**

Out[36]= {0.898858, 0.690018}

For both the lactate and white cell count we find p-values more than 0.05 and from this conclude that we cannot reject that the data comes from a population in which the variables are normally distributed.

Next, we can visualize the data as a scatter plot, with the "Lactate" variable on the horizontal and the "WCC" variable on the vertical axis.

Use the Thread function to create nested List objects to use as values for each marker:

In[37]:= **ListPlot[Thread[{lactate, wcc}], PlotRange → {6, 16},**
   PlotLabel → "Correlation between Lactate and White Cell Count Values",
   AxesLabel → {"Lacate", "WCC"}, PlotMarkers → {Automatic, Medium}]

Out[37]=

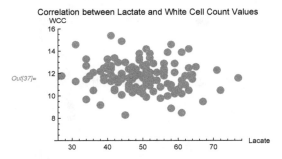

We can now use a test to check the correlation between the two variables.

Use the PearsonCorrelationTest function with the "TestDataTable" property:

In[38]:= **PearsonCorrelationTest[lactate, wcc, "TestDataTable"]**

Out[38]=

	Statistic	P-Value
Pearson Correlation	−0.128113	0.163175

We note a correlation coefficient of −0.13. This is a weak negative correlation. We see this reflected in the p-value, which is larger than the chosen α-value of 0.05. This means that we cannot reject the null hypothesis that the two variables are correlated.

Equation (1) below shows how we can calculate the correlation coefficient.

$$\rho = \frac{\text{Cov}(X, Y)}{\sigma_X \sigma_Y} \tag{1}$$

Here Cov is the covariance between the two variables and σ denotes the standard deviation of each.

Calculate the correlation coefficient:

In[39]:= **r = $\dfrac{\text{Covariance[lactate, wcc]}}{\text{StandardDeviation[lactate]} \times \text{StandardDeviation[wcc]}}$**

Out[39]= **−0.128113**

We can use the t distribution with degrees of freedom set to the sample size minus 2 to calculate the p-value. First, we use equation (2) to calculate a t-statistic.

$$t = r \sqrt{\frac{n - 2}{1 - r^2}} \tag{2}$$

Calculate the *t*-statistic:

$$In[40]:= \; t = r \sqrt{\frac{120-2}{1-r^2}}$$

$$Out[40]= -1.40323$$

From the next plot, we can see where the *t*-statistic falls on the probability density curve for 118 degrees of freedom.

Note that the parameters in StudentTDistribution[μ, σ, v] are μ (location), σ (scale), and v (degrees of freedom):

In[41]:= **Show[Plot[PDF[StudentTDistribution[120 – 2], x], {x, –10, 10}, Filling → Axis,**
PlotLabel → "*t* Distribution", PlotRange → {0, 0.4}], Graphics[Line[{{t, 0}, {t, 0.4}}]]]

Out[41]=

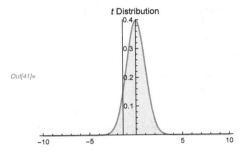

Since we have a two-tailed alternative hypothesis, we multiply the CDF by 2:

In[42]:= **CDF[NormalDistribution[0, 1], z] 2**

$$Out[42]= Erfc\left[-\frac{z}{\sqrt{2}}\right]$$

We can finally state that there is no correlation between the lactate and white cell count of our subjects ($r = -0.13$, $p = 0.16$).

Exercises

You can find the notebooks for this textbook at wolfr.am/klopper. All relevant .csv files are stored in the downloadable .zip file. If you are using a fresh notebook, make sure to have the .csv stored in the same folder.

15.1 Create a notebook in the same directory (or folder) as the spreadsheet file below and set it as the working directory.

15.2 Import the *SimulatedData.csv* file as a Dataset object named **data** and verify the integrity of the data by viewing the data from the first subject and also the number of subjects and variables.

15.3 Create a separate Dataset object for each of the two sample space elements in the "Group" variable and name them **coad** and **cb**.

15.4 Perform the required descriptive statistical analysis and visualization for the body mass index for the two groups of subjects. Perform the appropriate test to calculate the *p*-value for the difference in body mass indices between the two groups. What is the test conclusion for an α-value of 0.05?

15.5 Perform the relevant summary statistics and investigate the difference in levels of shortness of breath between the two groups.

15.6 Use the appropriate tests to investigate the difference in correlation between admission lactate levels and white cell count between the two groups.

Final Assessment

Well done. This text provides a good entry point to introductory statistics and the Wolfram Language. You do not need to be enrolled in a statistics course to gain enjoyment and use from this material—there are thousands of free databases filled with information that has likely never been analyzed.

Try some of the datasets at the Wolfram Data Repository. All data at the repository has been cleaned for use with the Wolfram Language and is readily available for analysis. Use it to write an article or a blog post or use it at your office with internal data.

The Wolfram Language is used by thousands of academics in the physical and social sciences, and it's well known to those who use other data science languages. There are hundreds of journals that accept Mathematica-based research, including Wolfram's own journals, *The Mathematica Journal* and *Complex Systems*. If you end up creating a neat bit of code, try submitting it to the Wolfram Demonstrations Project, or if you think your notebook is publishable in its own right, try submitting it to the Computational Notebook Archive. If you get into trouble and need a little help, Wolfram Community is a tight-knit group of Wolfram Language coders from all over the world who can help you with debugging.

Q&A

What is the Wolfram Demonstrations Project?

You've probably seen links to the Wolfram Demonstrations Project all through this book in the More to Explore sections. The Wolfram Demonstrations Project is a site comprised of user-submitted Demonstrations that use the Manipulate function to create interactive, visual representations on a wide range of topics. Currently there are over 12,000 Demonstrations available.

What are the Wolfram journals?

Wolfram Research runs two academic journals. The first is *The Mathematica Journal*, an online-only journal that publishes exemplary and novel uses of the Wolfram Language in various fields. The other is *Complex Systems*, a print journal with a more limited scope that focuses on "systems with simple components but complex overall behavior." Neither journal requires submission fees.

What is the Computational Notebook Archive?

It is a new service that publishes finished and unfinished notebooks that have value to the community and can be used in overlay journals like Elsevier's *SoftwareX*.

What is Wolfram Community?

It is a good place to post your questions. Professionals and academics from dozens of different fields post experimental, unfinished projects for review. Users may comment, borrow code, and add their own flair.

More to Explore

Check out the documentation pages on StandardVariation and StudentTDistribution for more details and interesting charts (wolfr.am/Documentation)

Here's an example of use from finance in a neat Wolfram Demonstration by P. Thiansathaporn (wolfr.am/ValueDistributions)

Another excellent resource for researchers and programmers is Wolfram Community. Here is the Community group for statistics (wolfr.am/Statistics)

Try this demonstration on the Mann–Whitney nonparametric test by O. E. Prokopchenko (wolfr.am/NonparametricTest)

Here is another research project using publicly available data on power outages in the UK (wolfr.am/PowerOutages)

Answers to Exercises

Almost all the exercises have many possible correct answers; what's listed here are merely sample correct answers. In most cases, we provide only the input code.

2 | Evaluating Basic Math

2.1   `1 + 4 + 14 + 14 − 3 + 2`

2.2   `Plus[1 , 4, 14, 14, −3 , 2]`

2.3   a. `5^2`

b. `27^1 / 3`

c. `10 000^1 / 2`

2.4   a. `Sqrt[9]`

b. `Sqrt[10 000]`

c. `Sqrt[2]`

`Sqrt[2] // N`

2.5   a. `Sin[0]`

b. `Sin[`$\frac{\pi}{3}$`]`

`Sin[Pi / 3]`

c. `Sin[`$\frac{\pi}{2}$`]`

2.6   `(10 + 12 + 14 + 12 + 13 + 10 + 9 + 16)/8`

Alternative method 1:

`Mean[{10, 12, 14, 12, 13, 10, 9, 16}]`

Alternative method 2:

`Total[{10, 12, 14, 12, 13, 10, 9, 16}] /`
`Length[{10, 12, 14, 12, 13, 10, 9, 16}]`

3 | Collections

3.1   `myList1 = {1, 2, 3, 4}`

3.2   `myList2 = {10, 11, 12, 13}`

3.3   `myList1 + myList2`

3.4   `myList1∗myList2`

3.5   `myCubes = Table[i^3, {i, 7}]`

3.6   `myCubes[[5]]`

3.7   `myPairs = Table[i + j, {i, 5}, {j, 2}]`

3.8   `MatrixForm@myPairs`

3.9   `myPairs[[;; , 2]]`

3.10 `myEvens = Table[2∗n, {n, 1, 10}]`

3.11 `Select[myEvens, ♯ < 10 &]`

3.12 `AppendTo[myEvens, Table[2∗n, {n, 11, 20}]] // Flatten`

4 | Working with Datasets

4.1   `dataset = Dataset[{`
`<|"a" -> 1,"b" ->" I","c"  -> 2|>,`
`<|"a" -> 2,"b" ->" II","c"  -> 3|>,`
`<|"a" -> 3,"b" ->" II","c"  -> 1|>,`
`<|"a" -> 4,"b" ->" I","c"  -> 1|>,`
`<|"a" -> 5,"b" ->" II","c"  -> 4|>,`
`<|"a" -> 6,"b" ->" I","c"  -> 2|>,`
`<|"a" -> 7,"b" ->" II","c"  -> 5|>,`
`<|"a" -> 8,"b" ->" II","c"  -> 6|>,`
`<|"a" -> 9,"b" ->" I","c"  -> 3|>,`
`<|"a" -> 10,"b" ->" I","c"  -> 2|>,`
`<|"a" -> 11,"b" ->" II","c"  -> 1|>,`
`<|"a" -> 12,"b" ->" I","c"  -> 5|>,`
`<|"a" -> 13,"b" ->" II","c"  -> 5|>}]`

4.2   `Dimensions[dataset]`

4.3   `dataset[[;;,2]]`

I	II	II	I	II	I
II	II	I	I	II	I
II					

Using the All keyword:

`dataset[[All, 2]]`

I	II	II	I	II	I
II	II	I	I	II	I
II					

4.4   `dataset[Select[♯c >= 4 &]]`

a	b	c
5	II	4
7	II	5
8	II	6
12	I	5
13	II	5

4.5   `dataset[[2 ;; 4, {"b", "c"}]]`

b	c
II	3
II	1
I	1

Using column numbers:

`dataset[[2 ;; 4, {2, 3}]]`

b	c
II	3
II	1
I	1

4.6 **dataset[[{2, 4}, {1, 3}]]**

a	c
2	3
4	1

4.7 **dataset[Mean, "c"] // N**

4.8 **variableC = Normal[dataset[List," c"]][[1]]**

5 | Data Types

5.1 **SetDirectory[NotebookDirectory[]];**
     chapter5Data = SemanticImport["Variables.csv"];
     chapter5Data[Counts, "InsulinDependentDiabetic"]

No	544
Yes	53

5.2 **chapter5Data[Counts, "SurveyQuestion1"]**

5	125
1	116
2	117
3	124
4	115

5.3 Nominal categorical.

5.4 Ratio-type numerical (continuous).

5.5 **chapter5Data[{Min, Max}," HB"]**

9.	20.

6 | Simple Descriptive Statistics

6.1 **variable = {5, 2, 9, 9, 3, 8, 6, 5, 5, 4, 7, 9, 8, 9, 3, 3, 3, 8, 1, 6}**

6.2 **Mean[variable] // N**

6.3 **Median[variable] // N**

6.4 **Tally[variable]**

{{5, 3}, {2, 1}, {9, 4}, {3, 4}, {8, 3}, {6, 2}, {4, 1}, {7, 1}, {1, 1}}

Using the **Counts** function:

Counts[variable]

<| 5 → 3, 2 → 1, 9 → 4, 3 → 4, 8 → 3, 6 → 2, 4 → 1, 7 → 1, 1 → 1 |>

The mode values are 3 and 9, each occurring 4 times.

6.5 **StandardDeviation[variable] // N**

6.6 **Min[variable]**

  Max[variable]

6.7 **Quartiles[variable] // N**

6.8 **InterquartileRange[variable]**

6.9 **Select[variable, # > 4 &]**

7 | Visualizing Data

7.1 **SetDirectory[NotebookDirectory[]];**
     chapter7Data = SemanticImport["Simulation.csv"];
     chapter7Data[ListPlot, {"Variable4", "Variable5"}]

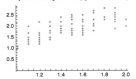

7.2 **variable6 = Normal[chapter7Data[List, "Variable6"]][[1]];**

7.3 **BoxWhiskerChart[variable6, "Mean"]**

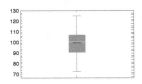

7.4 **Histogram[variable6, {10}]**

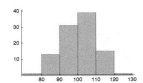

7.5 **variable4 = Normal[chapter7Data[List, "Variable4"]][[1]];**
     variable5 = Normal[chapter7Data[List, "Variable5"]][[1]];
     SmoothHistogram[{variable4, variable5}, Filling –> Axis]

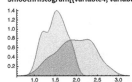

7.6 **category1 = Normal[chapter7Data[List, "Category1"]][[1]];**
     BarChart[Counts[category1]]

7.7 **PieChart[Counts[category1]]**

8 | Distributions

8.1 **tenSidedDie = RandomInteger[{1, 10}, 10000];**

8.2 **Histogram[tenSidedDie, Automatic, "Probability"]**

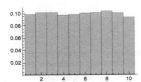

8.3 **tenSidedDice = RandomVariate[DiscreteUniformDistribution[{1, 10}], {20000, 2}];**

8.4 **totals = Plus @@@ tenSidedDice;**

8.5 **Histogram[totals, Automatic," Probability"]**

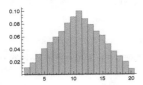

8.6 Eleven at a probability of around 10%.

8.7 **Plot[PDF[NormalDistribution[], x], {x, –6, 6}, Filling –> Axis]**

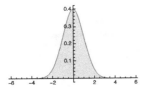

9 | Hypothesis Testing

9.1 **Needs["HypothesisTesting`"];**

9.2 **vals = RandomVariate[NormalDistribution[100, 20], 500];**

9.3 **Histogram[vals]**

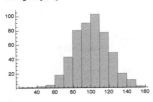

9.4 **Plot[PDF[NormalDistribution[Mean[vals], StandardDeviation[vals]/Sqrt[500]], x], {x, 95, 105}, Filling –> Axis, PlotRange –> All]**

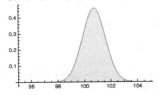

9.5 **MeanCI[vals]**

10 | Parametric Tests, Comparing Means

10.1 **group1 = RandomVariate[NormalDistribution[30, 5], 100];**
group2 = RandomVariate[NormalDistribution[30, 5], 100];
group3 = RandomVariate[NormalDistribution[30, 5], 100];

10.2 **Mean /@ {group1, group2, group3}**

StandardDeviation /@ {group1, group2, group3}

Quartiles /@ {group1, group2, group3}

{{26.975510577463773`, 30.782421046263657`, 34.92149710832944`},
{27.24353410413586`, 30.357398523224585`, 34.00927430015318`},
{26.617302191213504`, 30.00968970727476`, 33.75519213178116`}}

10.3 **BoxWhiskerChart[{group1, group2, group3}," Outliers", ChartLabels –> {"Group 1"," Group 2"," Group 3"}]**

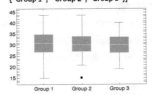

10.4 Selecting all absolute values larger than 3 or less than –3 for group1:

Select[Standardize[group1], # > 3 || # < –3 &]

Select[Standardize[group2], # > 3 || # < –3 &]

Select[Standardize[group3], # > 3 || # < –3 &]

10.5 **QuantilePlot[group1, NormalDistribution[]]**

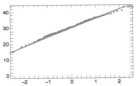

QuantilePlot[group2, NormalDistribution[]]

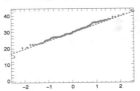

QuantilePlot[group3, NormalDistribution[]]

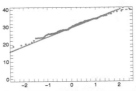

10.6 **ShapiroWilkTest /@ {group1, group2, group3}**

10.7 **TTest[{group1, group2}, 0," TestDataTable"]**

	Statistic	P-Value
T	0.236249	0.813484

10.8   Creating a list of the form {1, *value*} for group1 data point values:

```
anova = Table[{1, group1[[n]]}, {n, 1, Length[group1]}];
anova = Append[anova, Table[{2, group2[[n]]}, {n, Length[group2]}]]
anova = Append[anova, Table[{3, group3[[n]]}, {n, Length[group3]}]]
anova = Flatten[anova];
anova = Table[{anova[[n]], anova[[n + 1]]}, {n, 1, 599, 2}];
```

10.9   `Needs["ANOVA`"]`

```
ANOVA[anova]
```

11 | Correlation

11.1   `var1 = RandomVariate[NormalDistribution[100, 10], 30];`

11.2   `var2 = var1 + RandomVariate[NormalDistribution[5, 2], 30];`

11.3   Combining the pairs from var1 and var2:

```
var12 = Table[{var1[[n]], var2[[n]]}, {n, 1, Length[var1]}];
```

11.4   `ListPlot[var12]`

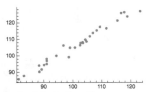

11.5   `r = Correlation[var1, var2]`

```
0.9869912243394047`
```

11.6 $zr = \dfrac{1}{2} Log[\dfrac{1+r}{1-r}];$

$zs = \dfrac{1}{\sqrt{30-3}};$

$z = \dfrac{zr}{zs}$

11.7   `Needs["HypothesisTesting`"];`
`NormalPValue[z, TwoSided -> True]`

```
TwoSidedPValue -> 5.212800157307882`*^-39
```

11.8   ```
lbzr = zr - (1.96 * zs);
upzr = zr + (1.96 * zs);
```
$lbr = \dfrac{Exp[2\ lbzr] - 1}{Exp[2\ lbzr] + 1}$

$ubr = \dfrac{Exp[2\ upzr] - 1}{Exp[2\ upzr] + 1}$

## 12 | Linear Regression

12.1   `SetDirectory[NotebookDirectory[]];`
`data = SemanticImport["LinearRegression.csv", Delimiters -> ","];`

12.2   `data[[;; 5]]`

| SubjectID | InputVariable | OutputVariable |
|-----------|---------------|----------------|
| 1 | 106 | 121 |
| 2 | 97 | 91 |
| 3 | 87 | 84 |
| 4 | 101 | 111 |
| 5 | 110 | 133 |

12.3   `data[ListPlot, {"InputVariable", "OutputVariable"}]`

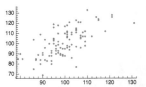

12.4   `inputVariable = Normal[data[List," InputVariable"]][[1]];`
`outputVariable = Normal[data[List," OutputVariable"]][[1]];`

12.5   `pairedVariables = Table[{inputVariable[[n]], outputVariable[[n]]},`
`{n, 1, Length[inputVariable]}];`

12.6   `linearModel = LinearModelFit[pairedVariables, x, x]`

FittedModel | 0.945536 + 1.00517 x |

12.7   `linearModel["ParameterTable"]`

|   | Estimate | Standard Error | t-Statistic | P-Value |
|---|----------|----------------|-------------|---------|
| 1 | 0.945536 | 11.5011 | 0.0822126 | 0.934645 |
| x | 1.00517 | 0.115044 | 8.73721 | 6.62052 $\times 10^{-14}$ |

12.8   `Show[ListPlot[pairedVariables], Plot[linearModel[x], {x, 80, 130}]]`

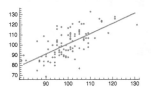

12.9   `SmoothHistogram[linearModel["FitResiduals"]]`

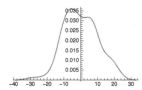

12.10  `linearModel["RSquared"]`

## 13 | Comparing Categorical Variables

13.1   `obs = {{87, 101, 31}, {88, 29, 99}};`

13.2   `rc = {{"GroupA","GroupB"},`
`{"ResponseA","ResponseB","ResponseC"}};`
`TableForm[obs, TableHeadings -> rc]`

|        | ResponseA | ResponseB | ResponseC |
|--------|-----------|-----------|-----------|
| GroupA | 87 | 101 | 31 |
| GroupB | 88 | 29 | 99 |

13.3   `fit = Outer[Times, Plus @@@ obs, Plus @@@`
`Transpose[obs]]/Plus @@ Flatten[obs];`
`fit // N // TableForm`

```
88.1034    65.4483    65.4483
86.8966    64.5517    64.5517
```

13.4   `residual = obs – fit;`
`residual // N // TableForm`

```
-1.103448275862069`    35.55172413793103`    -34.44827586206897`
1.103448275862069`    -35.55172413793103`    34.44827586206897`
```

13.5 $\chi 2array = \dfrac{residual^2}{fit};$
`TableForm[χ2array // N]`

```
0.013820095822930022`    19.311816431088985`    18.131626757748627`
0.014012041598248495`    19.580036103743`    18.383454907161802`
```
```

13.6   χ2 = Plus @@ Flatten[χ2array];
χ2 // N

13.7   dof = Length[Flatten[obs]] – Length[obs] – Length[Transpose[obs]] + 1

13.8   1 – CDF[ChiSquareDistribution[dof], χ2] // N

4.1643633730075835`*^–17

13.9   The /@ symbol is shorthand for applying a function to each
element in a list creating a List object:

$$\frac{\text{Times @@ Factorial /@ \{4, 5, 6, 3\}}}{\text{Times @@ Factorial /@ \{2, 2, 4, 1, 9\}}} \text{ // N}$$

14 | Nonparametric Tests

14.1   groupI = RandomInteger[RandomSeed[1234]; {90, 110}, 100];
groupII = groupI + RandomInteger[RandomSeed[1234]; {–10, 10}, 100];

14.2   QuantilePlot /@ {groupI, groupII}

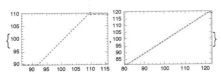

14.3   ShapiroWilkTest /@ {groupI, groupII}

14.4   BoxWhiskerChart[{groupI, groupII}, "Outliers"]

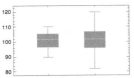

14.5   MannWhitneyTest[{groupI, groupII}, 0," TestDataTable"]

	Statistic	P-Value
Mann-Whitney	4990.5	0.980487

14.6   groupIII = RandomInteger[RandomSeed[1234]; {100, 140}, 100];

14.7   QuantilePlot[groupIII]

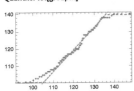

14.8   ShapiroWilkTest[groupIII]

14.9   BoxWhiskerChart[groupIII," Outliers"]

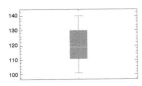

14.10   lists = Table[{groupI[[n]], groupII[[n]], groupIII[[n]]}, {n, 1, 100}];

14.11   LocationEquivalenceTest[lists, {"TestDataTable", "KruskalWallis"}]

$$\left\{\{\text{Null}\}, \left\{\begin{array}{c|cc} & \text{Statistic} & \text{P-Value} \\ \hline \text{Kruskal-Wallis} & 80.5373 & 0.94981 \end{array}\right\}\right\}$$

15 | A Research Project Demonstration

15.1   SetDirectory[NotebookDirectory[]];

15.2   data = SemanticImport["SimulatedData.csv"];

data[[1]]

Group	COAD
Age	70
BMI	21
SOB	Mild
Shock	Yes
MechanicalVentilation	Yes
Lactate	42
WCC	11.6
InHospitalMortality	No

Dimensions[data]

15.3   coad = data[Select[#Group == "COAD" &]];
cb = data[Select[#Group == "CB" &]];

15.4   data[GroupBy["Group"], {Min, Max, Mean, Median,
StandardDeviation,
InterquartileRange}, "BMI"]

| COAD | 14 | 36 | 25.6429 | 51/2 | |
| CB | 7 | 62 | 65/2 | 67/2 | |

coadBMI = Normal[coad[List, "BMI"]][[1]];
cbBMI = Normal[cb[List, "BMI"]][[1]];

BoxWhiskerChart[{coadBMI, cbBMI}, "Outliers",
PlotLabel –> "Difference in BMI for Each Group",
ChartLabels –> {"COAD", "CB"}]

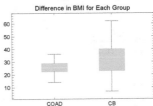

ShapiroWilkTest /@ {coadBMI, cbBMI}

TTest[{coadBMI, cbBMI}]

TTest[{coadBMI, cbBMI}, 0, "TestConclusion "]

The null hypothesis that the mean difference is 0 is rejected at
the 5 percent level based on the T test.

15.5   data[Tally, "SOB"]

Mild	50
Moderate	40
Severe	30

```
data[GroupBy["Group"], Counts, "SOB"]
```

COAD	Mild	19
	Severe	14
	Moderate	23
CB	Moderate	17
	Mild	31
	Severe	16

```
BarChart[{{19, 31}, {23, 17}, {14, 16}},
   ChartLegends -> {"COAD", "BMI"},
   PlotLabel -> "SOB Level for Each Group"]
```

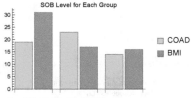

```
obs = {{19, 23, 14}, {31, 17, 16}}
```

```
rc = {{"COAD", "CB"}, {"Mild", "Moderate", "Severe"}}
```

```
TableForm[obs, TableHeadings → rc]
```

	Mild	Moderate	Severe
COAD	19	23	14
CB	31	17	16

```
fit = Outer[Times, Plus @@@ obs, Plus @@@ Transpose[obs]] / 120
```

$$\left\{\left\{\frac{70}{3}, \frac{56}{3}, 14\right\}, \left\{\frac{80}{3}, \frac{64}{3}, 16\right\}\right\}$$

```
TableForm[fit, TableHeadings → rc] // N
```

	Mild	Moderate	Severe
COAD	23.3333	18.6667	14.
CB	26.6667	21.3333	16.

```
residual = obs – fit
```

$$\left\{\left\{-\frac{13}{3}, \frac{13}{3}, 0\right\}, \left\{\frac{13}{3}, -\frac{13}{3}, 0\right\}\right\}$$

$$\chi2Array = \frac{residual^2}{fit}$$

$$\left\{\left\{\frac{169}{210}, \frac{169}{168}, 0\right\}, \left\{\frac{169}{240}, \frac{169}{192}, 0\right\}\right\}$$

```
dof = Length[Flatten[obs]] –
   Length[obs] – Length[Transpose[obs]] + 1
```

```
χ2 = Plus @@ Flatten[χ2Array];
χ2 // N
```

```
1 – CDF[ChiSquareDistribution[dof], χ2] // N
```

15.6
```
coadLactate = Normal[coad[List, "Lactate"]][[1]];
coadWCC = Normal[coad[List, "WCC"]][[1]];
cbLactate = Normal[cb[List, "Lactate"]][[1]];
cbWCC = Normal[cb[List, "WCC"]][[1]];
coad[{Min, Max, Mean, Median,
   StandardDeviation, InterquartileRange}, "Lactate"]
```

31	77	50.6071	51	9.

```
cb[{Min, Max, Mean, Median,
   StandardDeviation, InterquartileRange}, "Lactate"]
```

27	72	49.3281	99/2	9.4

```
coad[{Min, Max, Mean, Median,
   StandardDeviation, InterquartileRange}, "WCC"]
```

| 9.8 |
| 15.4 |
| 12.3875 |
| 12.4 |
| 1.2606 |
| 1.7 |

```
cb[{Min, Max, Mean, Median,
   StandardDeviation, InterquartileRange}, "WCC"]
```

| 8.3 |
| 13.4 |
| 11.2453 |
| 11.45 |
| 1.06814 |
| 1.35 |

```
ListPlot[{Thread[{coadLactate, coadWCC}],
   Thread[{cbLactate, cbWCC}]},
   PlotMarkers -> {Automatic, Medium},
   PlotLabel -> "Lactate vs WCC for Each Group",
   PlotLegends -> {"COAD", "CB"},
   AxesLabel -> {"Lacate", "WCC"}]
```

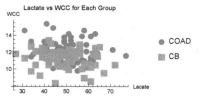

```
ShapiroWilkTest /@ {coadLactate, coadWCC, cbLactate, cbWCC}
```

```
PearsonCorrelationTest [
   coadLactate, coadWCC, "TestDataTable "]
```

	Statistic	P-Value
Pearson Correlation	−0.213807	0.11359

```
PearsonCorrelationTest [cbLactate, cbWCC, "TestDataTable "]
```

	Statistic	P-Value
Pearson Correlation	−0.142221	0.262266

Noting the correlation coefficients and p-values for the individual groups correlations, we can now test whether the difference in correlation between the two groups are significant. Our null hypothesis will be that there is no difference in the correlation coefficients and our alternative hypothesis is that there is a difference in these values.

Save the two correlation coefficients in computer variables.

```
rCOADLactateWCC = Correlation[coadLactate, coadWCC]
```

```
rCBLactateWCC = Correlation[cbLactate, cbWCC]
```

We can now use the equation shown to calculate a test statistic.

$$d_z = \frac{r_A - r_B}{\sqrt{\dfrac{1}{n_A - 3} + \dfrac{1}{n_B - 3}}}$$

$$dz = \frac{rCOADLactateWCC - rCBLactateWCC}{\sqrt{\dfrac{1}{Length[coad] - 3} + \dfrac{1}{Length[cb] - 3}}}$$

The test statistic is negative. We can use the **CDF** function to calculate a one-tailed *p*-value and multiply it by 2 for a two-tailed value.

CDF[NormalDistribution[0, 1], dz] 2

For Megan

I'd also like to convey my sincere gratitude to Jonathan Shock and Clemens Dempers for first introducing me to the Wolfram Language. You have always been there to answer my questions and have opened a wonderful world of knowledge-based computation. I'd also like to thank Malgorzata Konwerska at Wolfram Research for her thoughtful help with this book.

Index

Printed in the USA
CPSIA information can be obtained
at www.ICGtesting.com
LVHW081030171023
761014LV00096BA/1069